DISCLAIMER

The information presented in this reference book has been compiled from sources and documents believed to be reliable and represents the best professional judgement of TRAINCAN, Inc. However, the accuracy of the information presented is not guaranteed, nor is any responsibility assumed or implied by TRAINCAN, Inc. for any damage or loss resulting from inaccuracies or omissions.

The information and recommendations used in ADVANCED.*fst*® are based on the Canadian Food Retail and Food Services Regulation and Code (FRFSRC), Health Canada and The Canadian Food Inspection Agency.

Laws may vary greatly by city, municipality and province. This book is not intended to provide legal advice or establish standards of reasonable behaviour. Operators who develop food safety related policies and procedures as part of their commitment to employee and customer safety are urged to use the advice and guidance of legal counsel.

3rd Edition
Editing and Technical Writing
by Margaret Spence Krewen
Assisted by Mary Susan Douglas-Farache
Art Direction by David Heath

ADVANCED.*fst*® Manager Certification Coursebook
Copyright 2011
Updated April 2012

ISBN 978-0-920591-16-1

ADVANCED.*fst*® is a registered trademark of TRAINCAN, Inc.
85 Scarsdale Road, #101 Toronto, ON, M3B 2R2
Tel: (416) 447-9588
Toll free: 1-888-687-8796
Fax: (416) 646-0877
info@traincan.com
www.traincan.com

Printed in Canada.

ACKNOWLEDGEMENTS

The development of the ADVANCED.*fst*® Management Certification Coursebook would not have been possible without the contribution and co-operation of many industry, academic and public health representatives from across Canada. Representatives from the foodservice and food retail industry, trainers, and public health inspectors met and participated in focus groups to review this project.

Reviewers gave generously of their time to read and comment on ADVANCED.*fst*® 3rd Edition content. Recognizing that any such list is likely to be incomplete, TrainCan Inc. is pleased to thank the following people for the time and effort they dedicated to this and previous editions of ADVANCED.*fst*®.

Louise Blanchet

Victor Bulava

Steve Burns

Mike Byerley

Reg Carriere

Richard Carson

Micheline Chammaa

Jason Cheskes

Vince Chiodio

Guy Choquette

Catherine Crowe

Richard J. Davies

Sally de la Rue Browne

Maria Del Giacco

Diane Dessureault

Heli Donaldson

Paul-Guy Duhamel

Theresa Dunkley-Verhage

Bill Fitzpatrick

Jason Forbes

Kevin Freeborn

Robert Freeman

Samuel Glass

Darlene Hann

Gene Jochen

Monira Kayhan

Emile Lebel

Marilyn B. Lee

Andrew Lewis

Domenic Losito

Michele MacLean

Lisa Marsden

Scott Martin

Julianna McLeod

Gary Moulton

Chantal Picard

Chuck Poltz

Dan Reeves

Lana Schroeder-Wilk

Dr. Tim Sly

Robbie Stewart

Casey van den Heuvel

Keith Warriner

Theresa Wawrykow

Claudia Westland

Jim Wyatt

CONTENTS

INTRODUCTION

Whether you are a small restaurant, cafeteria, distributor or retail operator, your vision includes providing customers with wholesome, quality food in an inviting environment. To be successful, employees, food and equipment must be managed and co-ordinated every minute of every working day. The success of your operation relies on the support of skilled and dedicated people.

TRAINCAN, Inc. has designed the ADVANCED.*fst*® Certification Coursebook to help leaders in foodservice and food retail meet the challenges of a complex and demanding business. This book focuses on the provision of safe food and introduces ways to prevent food-related illnesses. ADVANCED.*fst*® will help you develop and implement a comprehensive food safety system for your operation.

As a leader in the food industry your main goals are:

1) Keeping people safe. It is the single most important reason for food safety. If your operation does not handle food carefully, the people you serve may get sick — or worse. Keeping customers and co-workers safe helps make your operation a better place to work and a place that keeps customers coming back.

2) Preventing food safety errors. Almost any food can become dangerous if not handled safely. Even professional operations — like yours — can make food handling errors if employees are not careful.

3) Protecting the bottom line. The health of your business can be directly related to the procedures and policies you implement in your day to day operation. Food safety incidents can be costly – both to your reputation and your financial wellness.

Food safety depends on every area of your foodservice operation working properly — from receiving the food at the loading dock to serving it to customers. You must do your part — but you cannot do it alone. You need to involve all of your employees. Working together for food safety — that is what it is all about.

What is ADVANCED.*fst*®?

ADVANCED.*fst*® is TRAINCAN's Canadian management level food safety program. It centres on the role of foodservice and food retail leaders in measuring risks, setting policies, and training and supervising employees.

The following support materials can be used with the ADVANCED.*fst* ® course book to deliver the program:

- Instructor CD * (Includes PowerPoint presentation, Instructor Guide and Scantron demonstration).

- Food Safety Self Audit Kit.

- Hand Washing Training Kit *.

- Food Safety Training Videos*.

- Glo Germ™ Products.

- Food Safety Face-Off Game*.

* *Available in French.*

Other materials available from TrainCan include:

- Allergen Training for the Foodservice and Food Retail Industry

- WHMIS for Hospitality Industry

- Applying HACCP™ Principles for The Food Service Industry

- Workplace Harassment Sensitivity Training

How to Use This Book

ADVANCED.*fst*® has been designed for self-study. Each chapter starts with a quick test to review your knowledge of the subject matter, and a set of learning objectives to guide you through the material. Key Word definitions can be found at the start of each chapter, and in the Glossary at the end of the book.

Each foodservice and food retail operation is unique and must follow company policies and local laws. Spaces have been provided throughout each chapter for you to make notes on policies, regulations and other important points that apply to you and your operation.

You will find exercises at the beginning and end of each chapter with an answer key at the back of the book. Complete the Test Your Food Safety IQ exercises before going to your course; not only will you understand the course better, they will help you do well on your certification exam. Continue to use your coursebook on the job to review food safety information.

Contents of the Certification Coursebook

Part I The Challenge to Food Safety covers the need for food safety, the hazards that threaten food and guidelines for training employees in personal hygiene.

Part II The Flow of Food covers methods for purchasing, receiving, storing, preparing, cooking, holding, serving, displaying, cooling and reheating food safely.

Part III Developing a Food Safety System covers the basics of a Hazard Analysis Critical Control Point (HACCP) food safety system and methods for training employees to run the system.

Part IV Maintaining Sanitary Facilities and Equipment covers designing facilities and choosing equipment, cleaning and sanitizing, and controlling pests. Tips for working with regulatory agencies are included.

The Benefits of Serving Safe Food

A well-designed food safety program protects your customers and fellow employees. Your operation's reputation will be secure. Repeat business from customers and increased job satisfaction among employees can lead to higher profits and better service.

You may benefit directly from reduced or minimized insurance costs. You will most likely benefit by reducing health violations and becoming less open to lawsuits claiming injury and negligence. Serving safe food is vital to the success of your operation.

Food Quality

Handling food safely helps preserve its appearance, flavour, texture, consistency, nutritional value and chemical properties. Food that is stored, prepared, served and presented properly is more likely to keep its fresh quality.

Profitability

Much of the success in foodservice and food retail is based on the consumers' experience and their word of mouth regarding that experience. Many of us have had someone complain that they thought the food made them ill. Every dissatisfied customer will likely tell 10 to 20 people about the experience. For every person who speaks up there are 26 who don't! If your average check or order is $10 and the customer who spoke up tells 10 others, that just cost you $100. If the 26 quiet types each tell 10 pals, that costs an additional $2,600!

Health Canada estimates between 11 to 13 million Canadians suffer from foodborne illness each year at a cost to the Canadian economy of over $12 billion.

The costs of an outbreak can be high. You may have to pay compensation for damages. If you can't prove that you have been committed to ensuring food is properly handled, you will likely also have to pay punitive damages. Other potential costs are lawyers' fees, costs for food testing at private laboratories, employee wages and disposal of food. Revenue, reputation and customers are also lost while you are closed for investigation.

Safe food handling can also lead to lower food costs through less waste. Employees' productivity may also improve when jobs are done properly the first time.

Liability

Today, customers are very willing to use lawsuits to obtain compensation for any injuries they feel they have suffered as a result of the food they were served. If you have a food safety program in place, you can use a reasonable care defence against a food-related lawsuit.

Reasonable care is based on proving that your operation had done everything that could be reasonably expected to prevent illness by ensuring that safe food was served. Written standards, procedures, and inspection results are the keys to this defence.

Marketing

Make it clear to your employees and customers that your operation takes food safety very seriously. Show your employees that:

- Top management is involved in and supports food safety policies.

- Food safety training for managers and all employees is a high priority. Training courses are offered, updated and evaluated regularly.

- Safe food handling procedures are documented, used in regular inspections and updated as necessary.

- Safe food handling is appreciated. Consider awarding certificates for training and giving out small rewards for good food safety records.

- You and other upper level management obey all food safety rules. Set a good example.

Show your customers that:

- Your employees know and follow food safety rules. Use items like place mats and posters to get your message across. Award employees with pins and buttons to wear outside of food preparation and service areas. Be sure your employees can answer simple food safety questions from customers.

- Customers can help keep food safe. Use your carry-out packaging to urge customers to safely handle their food. Station employees near self-serve areas so they can help customers avoid inadvertently contaminating food.

Regulation

The standards, temperatures and other regulatory information mentioned in this book are based on the Canadian Food Inspection Agency (CFIA) and Health Canada requirements and the Canadian Food Retail and Food Services Regulation and Code (FRFSRC). These are the suggested minimum requirements in Canada; they may differ from local and provincial/territorial regulations.

ADVANCED.*fst*® refers to the Canadian Food Retail and Food Services Code (FRFSC) because it consists of model requirements for safeguarding public health and assuring food safety. The Code provides practical, user friendly interpretations and guidance for compliance with legislation.

Health Canada sets policies and standards governing the safety and nutritional quality of all food sold in Canada.

The Canadian Food Inspection Agency (CFIA) enforces these policies and standards.

Health Canada, the CFIA, the Public Health Agency of Canada and local public health authorities work together to prevent and when necessary, to respond to the outbreaks of foodborne illness.

Your premises must comply with municipal, provincial/ territorial and federal requirements to stay in operation. The health department overseeing your facility has the power to levy fines or close any operation that serves unsafe food or has numerous, documented legislation violations. Therefore, it is in everyone's best interest to work with their local Public Health Inspectors.

What a Food Safety Leader Needs to Know

Regional and provincial/territorial health departments hold the person "in charge" responsible for knowing and applying the following information:

- The diseases that are carried or transmitted by food, including their signs and symptoms.

- Points in the flow of food where hazards can be prevented, eliminated or reduced and how the procedures meet the requirements of the local legislation.

- The relationship between personal hygiene and the spread of disease, particularly cross-contamination, hand contact with ready-to-eat foods and handwashing.

- How to keep injured or ill employees from contaminating food or food contact surfaces.

- The length of time that potentially hazardous foods may remain at temperatures where disease-causing micro-organisms can grow.

- Safe cooking temperatures and times for potentially hazardous foods such as meat, poultry, eggs and fish.

- Proper temperatures and times for the safe refrigerated storage, hot holding, cooling and reheating of potentially hazardous foods.

- Correct procedures for cleaning and sanitizing utensils and food contact surfaces of equipment.

- The types of poisonous and toxic materials used in the operation and how to safely store, dispense, use and dispose of them.

- The need for equipment that is sufficient in number and capacity; and, properly designed, constructed, located, installed, operated, maintained and cleaned.

- The source of the operation's water supply and the importance of keeping it clean and safe.

- How the operation complies with the principles of a HACCP-based food safety system, as some local health departments require a HACCP system.

- The rights, responsibilities and authorities the local legislation assigns to employees, managers/operators, and the local health department.

The list is a long one! However, as you will see throughout this coursebook, each of these requirements is covered by common sense, and a logical and complete plan for food safety.

International Food Safety Icons

In an effort to create universal recognition of food safety hazards, the International Association for Food Protection (IAFP) has created the symbols shown below. While some symbols do not represent temperature recommendations put forth by the Canadian Food Retail and Food Services Regulation and Code (FRFSRC), they are provided here as an example of excellent visual tools. They are easy to recognize and understand regardless of language spoken. Symbols such as these should be used where possible throughout an operation as a procedural reminder.

Temperature Danger Zone

Refrigeration/Cold Holding

Cooling

Hot Holding

Do Not Work If Ill

Hand Washing

Cross Contamination

Wash, Rinse, Sanitize

No Bare Hand Contact

Potentially Hazardous Food

Cooking

Icons are reprinted with the permission of the International Association of Food Protection.

THE CHALLENGE TO FOOD SAFETY

PART 1.0

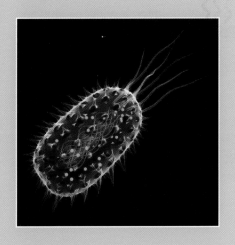

CHAPTER 1

TEST YOUR FOOD SAFETY

IQ

1. **True or False:** Tofu is not a potentially hazardous food. (*See Foods Most Likely to Become Contaminated, page 11*)

2. **True or False:** Hands can be a source of cross-contamination. (*See Cross-Contamination, page 14*)

3. **True or False:** Toxic metals that leach through worn cookware are a physical hazard. (*See How Food Becomes Unsafe, page 13*)

4. **True or False:** Outbreaks of foodborne illness can be caused by improper cooling of food. (*See Factors Most Often Named in Foodborne Outbreaks page 16*)

5. **True or False:** Food contact surfaces include splash areas. (*See Cross-Contamination, page 15*)

The Challenge to Food Safety

Canada's food safety system is internationally recognized as one of the safest in the world. Our status as a leader in producing, serving and selling safe, quality food is secure as long as we all commit to applying sound principles of food safety.

Foodborne illness has long been a challenge for all levels of the food industry and continues to pose a threat to employees and customers alike. Foodborne illness, or food poisoning, is caused by diseases that are carried or transmitted to people by food. *Salmonella* and *E. coli* are two of the best known types. Chapter 2 contains information on these and other specific illnesses.

The Laboratory Centre for Disease Control and Prevention (LCDC) defines an outbreak of foodborne illness as "an incident in which two or more people experience the same illness after eating the same food". Laboratory analysis should identify the food item as the illness source.

As a manager/operator/store owner, you are faced with the challenge of preventing outbreaks because of the:

- Number and types of foods at risk.

- Multiple chances for food to become contaminated. Food is at risk at every stage in the *flow of food* – the path that foods in your operation follow from receiving through storing, preparing, cooking, holding, serving, cooling and reheating.

LEARNING OBJECTIVES

After completing this chapter, you should be able to:

- Recognize the challenges to food safety in your operation.
- Discuss the main types of contamination.
- Identify the foods most likely to become contaminated.
- Recognize how food becomes contaminated.

TERMS TO KNOW

Clean: Free of visible soil and food waste.

Contamination: The unintended presence of harmful substances or micro-organisms in food.

Cross-Contamination: The transfer of harmful substances or micro-organisms to food from other foods, people or surfaces.

Flow of Food: The path that food follows throughout a foodservice or food retail operation.

Food Contact Surfaces: Any equipment, utensil or surface which normally comes in contact with food or which may drain, drip or splash in food or on to surfaces normally in contact with food.

Foodborne Illness: A disease caused by the ingestion of contaminated food.

High Risk Populations: People who have a greater risk of developing foodborne illness due to weakened immune systems.

Indirect Transmission: Harmful substances travel from one surface or food to another.

Outbreak: An incident in which two or more people experience the same illness after eating the same food.

Potentially Hazardous Food: A food that easily supports the growth of bacteria.

Ready-to-Eat Food: Prepared food that will not be cooked or re-cooked before serving.

Sanitary: Free from harmful levels of contamination.

- Type of customer you are serving. Children, elderly people, pregnant women and people with weakened immune systems are at the greatest risk for foodborne illness. These *high risk populations* are less able to fight off disease and, therefore, are more susceptible to illness.

- Shortage of employees trained in food safety and a high employee turn over.

The bottom line is that foodservice and food retail leaders are responsible for making sure that the food they offer to customers is safe. Therefore, a good food safety system and a strong training program are vital.

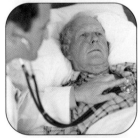

Foods Most Likely to Become Contaminated

While any food can become contaminated, foods most likely to be contaminated are *potentially hazardous foods* and *ready-to-eat foods*. Potentially hazardous foods are defined by the FRFSC as any perishable food capable of supporting rapid and progressive growth of infectious or toxigenic micro-organisms (*See Figure 1.0*). These are usually moist, high-protein foods that consist in whole or part of:

- Milk and milk products.

- Shell eggs.

- Meats and poultry.

FIGURE 1.0 POTENTIALLY HAZARDOUS FOODS

Milk and Milk Products

Shell Eggs

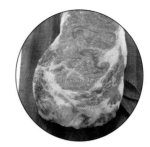

Beef

Poultry

Pork

Lamb

Fish

Sprouts

Shellfish

Soy-Protein Foods

Melons (Sliced)

Cooked Rice, Beans, Potatoes, or
Other Heat-Treated Plant Foods

Tofu

Garlic-and-Oil Mixtures

Stew/Soup

Food borne Illness.
Out break

Challenges
flow of food
High Risk population Infant
pregnant men
Elderly people
people taken certain
medicine
Cweekend Immune
system

- Fish and shellfish (molluscs and crustaceans, such as shrimp, lobster, crab).

- Tofu or other soy protein foods.

- Garlic and oil mixtures.

- Baked or boiled potatoes, cooked vegetables and other plant foods that have been heat-treated.

- Gravies, soups, stews, custards.

- Raw seeds and sprouts.

- Sliced melons and other cut fruit.

- Synthetic ingredients - such as textured soy protein in hamburger supplement.

According to the FRFSC, ready-to-eat foods are foods that do not require any further preparation before being consumed, except perhaps washing, thawing or moderate reheating.

How Food Becomes Unsafe

Contamination

Contamination refers to the unintended presence of harmful substances or micro-organisms in food. While these substances can be natural to food, as in the case of allergens, most contamination occurs when substances or micro-organisms accidentally get into food. Contaminants, or hazards, are broken down into three main types:

Biological hazards: These are living organisms that can multiply and grow. The four categories of biological hazards are bacteria, viruses, parasites and fungi (*See Figure 1.1*). Bacteria are the greatest threat to food safety.

Chemical hazards: These are toxic substances that may occur naturally, pesticides, food additives and preservatives, cleaning supplies, and toxic metals that leach through worn cookware and equipment (*See Figure 1.2*).

FIGURE 1.1 Biological Hazards

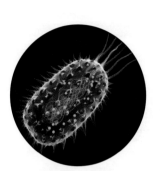

Bacteria

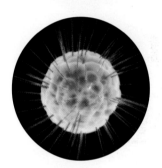

Viruses

Parasites

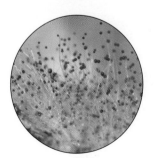

Fungi

FIGURE 1.2 Chemical Hazards

FIGURE 1.3 Physical Hazards

Metal shavings in an opened can may contaminate the food inside.

Physical hazards: These are foreign matter — such as dirt, broken glass and crockery, and other objects — that accidentally get into the food (*See Figure 1.3*).

Cross-Contamination

Disease can also be spread by *cross-contamination (Indirect transmission)*. Cross-contamination describes how harmful substances, such as micro-organisms and allergens, travel from one surface or food to another (*See Figure 1.4*). Cross-contamination happens when a safe food comes in contact with:

• A contaminated food (example – meat juices dripping on another food).

• A food handler who is carrying the harmful substance on their hands.

• A piece of equipment (such as a cutting board) that has the harmful substance on the surface.

Cross-contamination is most serious when micro-organisms travel from raw food on to ready-to-eat food. Even though the ready-to-eat food looks safe, it isn't. Specific instances of cross-contamination include examples such as:

• Hands that touch raw food and then cooked or ready-to-eat foods.

• Food surfaces that come into contact with raw food, are not cleaned and sanitized, and then contact ready-to-eat food.

• Cleaning cloths and sponges that touch raw food, equipment or utensils, are not cleaned and sanitized, and are then used on surfaces, equipment and utensils for ready-to-eat foods.

• Raw or contaminated foods that touch or drip fluids on cooked or ready-to-eat foods.

• Adding raw, contaminated ingredients to food that receives no further cooking.

FIGURE 1.4 Cross-Contamination

Never mix raw product with ready-to-eat product.

FIGURE 1.5 Clean Vs. Sanitary

Kitchen looks clean to the naked eye.

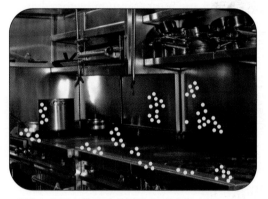

This photo shows bacteria that can remain
if sanitizing is not completed.

Food contact surfaces include any equipment or utensil surface which normally comes in contact with food or which may drain, drip, or splash in food or on surfaces normally in contact with food. Cutting boards, knives and splash areas are examples of food contact surfaces.

Clean vs. Sanitary

There is a distinct difference between *clean* and *sanitary*. Clean typically means free of visible soil, food residue and other foreign material, while sanitary means free of harmful levels of contamination (*See Figure 1.5*). It is important that people who work in the food industry understand the difference between clean and sanitary. Clean food, equipment and utensils may not be sanitary. For example, a glass may look sparkling clean but still carry harmful bacteria and chemicals. After being washed in boiling water, the same glass may now appear cloudy and watermarked - but it is sanitary.

Sanitizing is therefore best defined as the use of heat or chemicals to destroy 99.99% of the disease-causing micro-organisms on a food contact surface.

Factors Most Often Named in Foodborne Outbreaks

The following is a list of the most common factors that cause foodborne outbreaks. All these factors need to be controlled when designing your food safety system. Reported cases of foodborne illness usually involve more than one of these factors.

- Failure to properly cool food (one of the leading causes of foodborne outbreaks).

- Failure to thoroughly heat, or cook food.

- Infected employees who practice poor personal hygiene at home and work.

- Preparing food a day or more in advance of being served.

- Adding raw, contaminated ingredients to food that receives no further cooking.

- Allowing foods to stay too long at temperatures favourable to bacterial growth.

- Failure to reheat cooked foods to temperatures that kill bacteria.

- Cross-contamination of cooked food by raw food, improperly cleaned and sanitized equipment, or employees who mishandle food.

All these points can be divided into three broad categories: time and temperature abuse, poor personal hygiene, and cross-contamination.

Summary

- Foodborne illness is a major concern to the food industry.

- A well designed food safety program protects your customers, employees and your reputation.

- High-risk populations such as children, pregnant women, the elderly and the sick are more susceptible to foodborne illness than others.

- Identify potentially hazardous foods and take great care to avoid contamination. Control time and temperature at every step.

- Potentially hazardous foods and ready-to-eat foods are considered high-risk items.

- Biological, chemical and physical hazards, allergens and cross-contamination all pose a threat to the health of consumers.

- A food contact surface can look clean but not be sanitized — leading to foodborne illness.

- Make sure food is stored, prepared, cooked, held, served, cooled and reheated using methods that ensure its safety.

- Train staff to monitor, reinforce and maintain food safety principles.

- Establishing a well designed food safety system can help protect your customers by preventing outbreaks of foodborne illness and help the establishment avoid the potentially high costs associated with them.

Consider This....

Members of a popular punk rock band, the United Postal Workers, were among the 150 people stricken with foodborne illness during an outbreak on April 30th.

Written into their contract, the band always receives turkey sandwiches with no crusts, bottled water and a bowl of blue Smarties prior to their concert. A local restaurant, Sadie's, prepared the meal. This time, the delicious lunch turned disastrous for the band, resulting in an illness that triggered the cancellation of two weeks worth of concerts. Since all of the Sadie's patrons who were ill had also eaten turkey sandwiches, turkey was identified as the food most likely to have contained the disease-causing micro-organisms - leaving the United Postal Workers close to the bathroom, and their fans angry.

An investigation determined that the lunch the United Postal Workers and Sadie's patrons ate on April 27th was not prepared properly. Two days before, eight fresh turkeys had been delivered to Sadie's, but the kitchen staff had forgotten to put them away and they sat at the back door for five hours. The chef caught the mistake and placed the turkeys in the cooler. The next day all the turkeys were cooked and one temperature reading was taken from the smallest bird. The turkeys were then cooled, and carved. The slices were refrigerated overnight and taken out early the next morning to make the sandwiches. As one of the food handlers really wanted to meet the band, he came in to work early, feeling a bit queasy from the night before, made the sandwiches, completed his other line preparations for two hours (and left the sandwiches unrefrigerated) and then drove the sandwiches to the United Postal Workers.

A sample from the turkey eaten by both the band and restaurant patrons was tested and harmful bacteria were found in sufficient numbers to cause the illness. The food handler who prepared the sandwiches also tested positive for the bacteria.

What do you think happened here?

Answers can be found on page 200.

EXERCISE 1

1. **Foodborne illnesses are diseases that are:**
   a. Carried or transmitted to people by food.
   b. Caused by overeating.
   c. Cured by proper eating habits.
   d. Transmitted to kitchen employees only.

2. **Contamination refers to the:**
   a. Failure to cook food to the proper temperature to kill bacteria.
   b. Mistake of preparing food one day or more in advance of being served.
   c. Unintended presence of harmful substances or micro-organisms in food.
   d. Accidental mixing of uncomplimentary foods.

3. **Cross-contamination is the:**
   a. Main cleaning method for all food contact surfaces that have been contaminated.
   b. Transfer of harmful substances or micro-organisms to food from food or from a non-food contact surface, such as equipment, utensils, or hands.
   c. Removal of certain bacteria from food by cooking it thoroughly.
   d. Prevention of foodborne illness.

4. **The factors most often linked to unsafe food are:**
   a. Time and temperature abuse.
   b. Cross-contamination.
   c. Poor personal hygiene.
   d. All of the above.

5. **Dirt, broken glass and staples from packaging are classified as:**
   a. Chemical hazards.
   b. Biological hazards.
   c. Physical hazards.
   d. Bacterial hazards.

6. **From receiving to storing, preparing, cooking, holding, serving, cooling and reheating is called the:**
   a. Preparation of food.
   b. Cycle of food.
   c. Activity of food.
   d. Flow of food.

7. **People who are very young, or are already weak or ill, are seriously threatened by foodborne illness because they:**
   a. Cannot take strong medicine.
   b. Cannot tell the doctor what is wrong with them.
   c. Cannot fight off the disease very well.
   d. Are unable to file lawsuits.

8. **Sanitary can be defined as:**
   a. Free of visible soil, food residue and other foreign material.
   b. Free of harmful levels of contamination.
   c. Well wiped with soap and water.
   d. Fresh smelling.

Answers can be found on page 198.

Biological Hazards

*B*iological hazards are living organisms that can grow and cause disease. Sources of biological hazards include *bacteria*, *viruses*, insects, plants, birds, animals, fish and humans. Foodborne micro-organisms pose a threat to food safety because they are so tiny that they can only be seen by a microscope. Once in food, some of these hazards may be very hard to kill or control because some are able to survive freezing and high cooking temperatures. While not all micro-organisms cause disease, some do. These are called *pathogens*. Eating food contaminated with foodborne pathogens, or their *toxins*, is the leading cause of foodborne illness.

Bacteria

Of all micro-organisms, bacteria are of the greatest concern to the food industry. Bacteria are living single-celled organisms. They are so small that they can hitch a ride on everything from dust particles in the air to insects, plants, animals and people. Bacteria survive on skin and clothes, as well as in human hair, scabs, scars, the mouth, nose, throat and intestines. For these reasons, they can spread very quickly throughout a foodservice or food retail operation.

Some bacteria are beneficial (as found in yogurt), some cause food spoilage, and some are inactive. However, other bacteria may be:

• **Pathogenic** (infectious, disease-causing). These bacteria can cause illness and sometimes death in humans. They feed on potentially hazardous foods and can multiply very

TEST YOUR FOOD SAFETY

1. **True or False:** Some viruses can survive cooking and freezing. (*See Viruses, page 25*)

2. **True or False:** Mould only grows on surface environments; it does not penetrate the product. (*See Moulds, page 26*)

3. **True or False:** Severe vomiting and diarrhea are possible signs of a food allergy. (*See Food Allergens, page 33*)

4. **True or False:** Bacteria can only be carried inside the body of a person or animal. (*See Bacteria, page 19*)

5. **True or False:** Pathogens are micro-organisms that cause disease. (*See Biological Hazards, page 19*)

LEARNING OBJECTIVES

After completing this chapter, you should be able to:
● Identify biological, chemical and physical hazards (dangers).
● Describe how bacteria reproduce and grow.
● Discuss the factors needed for bacteria to grow.
● Know the Temperature Danger Zone and why it is important to keep foods out of it.

● Identify allergens and their importance to serving safe food.
● List ways to prevent allergens from harming customers.
● Discuss common allergens and common symptoms.
● Explain what to do in an emergency.

TERMS TO KNOW

Allergy: A condition of heightened sensitivity to certain things such as food.

Anaphylaxis: A severe allergic reaction that may result in death.

Bacteria: Living single-celled organisms that are most often the cause of foodborne illness.

Biological Hazard: Contamination of food by micro organisms.

Chemical Hazard: Contamination of food by chemical substances normally found in foodservice and food retail establishments.

FAT-TOM: An acronym for conditions favourable for the growth of bacteria: Food, Acidity, Time, Temperature, Oxygen and Moisture.

Foodborne Infection: An illness that is the direct result of consuming food containing harmful living micro-organisms. Symptoms usually do not appear right away.

Foodborne Intoxication: Results from consuming food containing toxins. The toxin may have been produced by harmful bacteria found on the food or be the result of a chemical contamination. Symptoms usually appear within a few hours.

Fungi: A group of micro-organisms that includes moulds, yeasts and mushrooms.

Parasite: A micro-organism that needs to live in or on a host to survive.

Pathogen: A disease-causing micro-organism.

Physical Hazard: Contamination that results from the accidental introduction of foreign objects into food.

Protozoa: Single-celled parasitic organisms found in soil and water.

Re-work: To recycle processed food.

Spores: Thick protective structures formed by certain bacteria in response to adverse conditions.

Temperature Danger Zone: The temperature range between 4°C and 60°C (40°F to 140°F) within which most bacteria grow and reproduce easily.

Toxigenic Bacteria: These bacteria produce harmful toxins as they multiply, die and/or break down; they are also pathogenic.

Toxin: Poisons produced by micro-organisms that are carried by fish or released by plants.

Toxin-Mediated Infection: This occurs when a person eats a food that contains pathogens which then produce illness-causing toxins in the intestines.

Virus: One of the smallest and simplest micro-organisms.

quickly under favourable circumstances. A disease-causing micro-organism is often referred to as a pathogen.

- **Toxigenic** (poisonous). These bacteria produce harmful toxins as they multiply, die and break down; they are also pathogenic.

Bacteria and the toxins they produce do not have an odour or taste to help you detect them. You cannot tell if they are in food. This is why it is so important to keep them out of food and keep them from multiplying.

How Bacteria Reproduce

Bacteria can exist in two different forms: the vegetative state and the *spore* state. Bacteria normally exist as vegetative cells, which can grow and reproduce. When in this state, the bacteria can survive low temperatures, even freezing, but can be killed by high temperature. These cells reproduce by dividing in two (*See Figure 2.0*). Then, each of those cells divides into two more cells, and so on.

FIGURE 2.0 Bacterial Growth

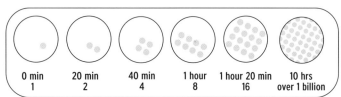

0 min	20 min	40 min	1 hour	1 hour 20 min	10 hrs
1	2	4	8	16	over 1 billion

As a result, bacteria can multiply very quickly. This rapid rate of reproduction increases the risk of foodborne illness.

Some kinds of bacteria can change into a different form called spores. In this state, they have very thick walls that protect them from an inhospitable environment. This means that spores survive cooking or freezing temperatures, high acidity, high salt conditions and some sanitizing mixtures. Spores do not grow or reproduce but they can become vegetative again within minutes when living conditions improve. The bacteria can once again grow and reproduce.

Since spores are difficult to destroy, it is important to cook, cool, and reheat food properly.

Multiple Barriers Control Bacterial Growth

As *FAT-TOM* shows (*See page 23*), several common conditions support bacterial growth. These conditions can occur at any point in the flow of food. That is, whenever food is received, stored, thawed, prepared, cooked, held, served, cooled or reheated.

To control contamination set up barriers that will reduce the conditions of FAT-TOM, such as raising or lowering the temperature of food to keep it out of the danger zone or pre-chilling recipe ingredients. The goal is to lower the risk that a single food-handling error will let bacteria grow enough to cause an illness.

Temperature control is an effective means of preventing, or at least limiting, bacterial growth. The time factor must also be used as a control. To use time as a control, you must:

- Mark food with the time/date it will be cooked, served, sold or discarded.

- Serve or discard food within two hours from the time it is removed from temperature control.

FIGURE 2.1 Temperature Danger Zone

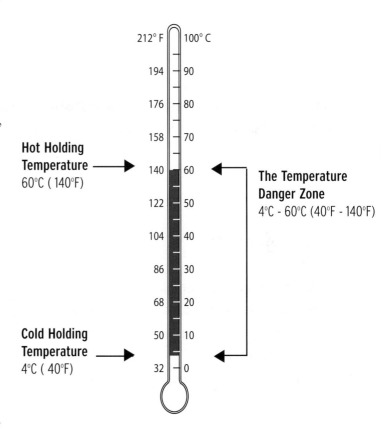

Hot Holding Temperature 60°C (140°F)

Cold Holding Temperature 4°C (40°F)

The Temperature Danger Zone 4°C - 60°C (40°F - 140°F)

THE MOST IMPORTANT FACTORS TO CONTROL ARE TEMPERATURE AND TIME.

- Discard unmarked or time expired containers or packages of food.

- Develop written procedures; keep them in your foodservice/food retail operation, and make them available to your local Public Health Inspector.

Foodborne Illnesses Caused by Bacteria

Figure 2.3 lists the major foodborne illnesses caused by bacteria. To get the most use from this table, review the following terms:

Foodborne Infection: A disease that results from eating food containing harmful micro-organisms. Diseases such as Salmonellosis, Shigellosis, and Listeriosis are foodborne infections.

Foodborne Intoxication: A disease that results from eating food containing toxins from bacteria, moulds, or certain plants or animals, such as mushrooms or puffer fish. *Staphylococcus* and *Clostridium botulinum* are foodborne intoxications.

Toxin-Mediated Infection: A disease that results from eating food contaminated with harmful micro-organisms. These micro-organisms grow inside the body and form toxins. *Bacillus cereus*, *Clostridium perfringens* and *Escherichia coli* 0157:H7 are examples of toxin-mediated infections.

Incubation Period: The time between the consumption of contaminated food and the appearance of symptoms of illness.

Duration of Illness: How long the illness lasts.

Symptoms: The physical signs of the disease.

Source: A host, carrier, or vehicle for disease-causing micro-organisms. A host is a person, animal, or plant on which another organism lives and feeds. A carrier is a person or animal whose body carries a disease-causing micro-organism. A vehicle is an item, such as wind, water, human hands, or dirty utensils, that carries or transports disease-causing micro-organisms.

Foods Involved: Foods that are known to carry or transmit the disease.

Spore Former: States if the bacteria form spores.

Prevention: How the spread of the disease may be stopped.

Bacillus cereus

Most foodborne illnesses are caused by bacteria, resulting in infection, intoxication or toxin-mediated infection. *Bacillus cereus* is of concern because two different toxins are involved, resulting in two different types of foodborne illness in humans – emetic (vomiting) and diarrheal.

Bacillus cereus is a spore-forming bacterium found widely in nature, including dust, dirt, crops, etc. The emetic form (intoxication) occurs very shortly after eating contaminated food, with an onset time of 0.5 to 6 hours. Starchy foods such as rice or potatoes are commonly associated with *Bacillus cereus* emetic toxin outbreaks. Fried rice is one of the most common foods for transmission because of its preparation process. *Bacillus cereus* emetic spores are more resistant to heat and chemical treatments than vegetative pathogens like *Salmonella*, *Esherichia coli*, *Campylobacter jejuni* and *Listeria monocytogenes*.

The diarrheal form (toxin-mediated) has a longer incubation period, with an onset time of between 6 and 15 hours. Unlike the *Bacillus cereus* emetic toxin, the diarrheal toxin is normally destroyed in the cooking process. Diarrhea-causing strains have been found in a wider selection of foods including meats, vegetables, soups and milk products. As you will note in the chart on page 29, careful time and temperature control, including proper cooling, is key to preventing FBI caused by both forms of Bacillus cereus.

What Bacteria Need to Grow

Bacteria can live anywhere a human can live. Generally, bacteria live well in potentially hazardous foods because these foods are often warm, moist, protein-rich, and neutral or low in acid. These favourable conditions can be remembered by the acronym FAT-TOM:

F FOOD High-protein foods may be received already contaminated and are at risk for contamination in the flow of food.

A ACIDITY Acidity is measured on a scale from 0 (very acid) to 14.0 (very alkaline [basic]). A solution with a pH (acid-alkaline measurement) of 7.0 is neutral (*See Figure 2.2a*). Most potentially hazardous foods have a pH level between 4.6 and 7.5. However, high acid foods, such as citrus fruit, rarely allow the growth of harmful bacteria.

T TIME Foodborne micro-organisms take time to grow to levels high enough to make someone ill. At room temperature, bacteria can double in number every ten to twenty minutes. Foods left in the *Temperature Danger Zone* for two to four hours can develop enough bacteria to cause foodborne illness.

T TEMPERATURE The Temperature Danger Zone* for potentially hazardous foods is 4°C to 60°C (40°F to 140°F) (*See Figure 2.1*). Exposing bacteria to temperatures outside the danger zone doesn't always kill them. Refrigeration, for example, is not total protection against bacterial growth as it may only slow it down. Discard food if it is past its expiration date.

O OXYGEN Some bacteria require oxygen to grow, while others require no oxygen. However, most of the bacteria that cause foodborne illness can grow either with or without oxygen.

M MOISTURE The amount of available water in food is called the water activity (a_w). A food with an (a_w) level of 0.85 or lower is not considered potentially hazardous. Most potentially hazardous foods have water activity values of 0.97-0.99, which is ideal for bacterial growth (*See Figure 2.2b*). Water activity can be reduced to safer levels by freezing, dehydrating (removing the water), adding sugar or salt, or cooking. Dry foods, such as beans and rice, become potentially hazardous when water is added.

* The FRFSC states that the Temperature Danger Zone is 4°C to 60°C (40°F to 140°F) . Some provincial/territorial or local regulations may use a slightly different temperature range. Check your local jurisdiction to find out what temperatures are accepted.

TEMPERATURE DANGER ZONE

In my jurisdiction the following temperature range is designated: _____

FIGURE 2.2a pH Scale

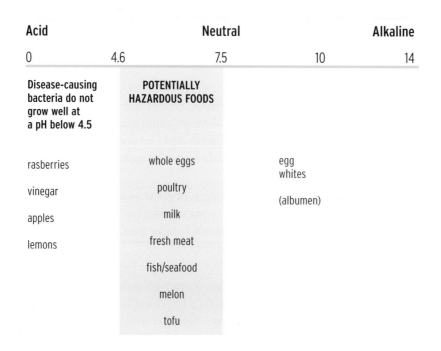

Acid		Neutral		Alkaline
0	4.6	7.5	10	14

Disease-causing bacteria do not grow well at a pH below 4.5

POTENTIALLY HAZARDOUS FOODS

rasberries	whole eggs	egg whites
vinegar	poultry	(albumen)
apples	milk	
lemons	fresh meat	
	fish/seafood	
	melon	
	tofu	

FIGURE 2.2b Water Activity of Some Common Foods

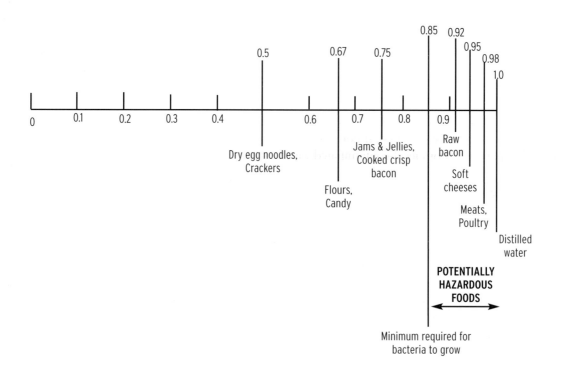

Viruses

Foodborne viruses differ from foodborne bacteria. Viruses are one of the smallest and simplest forms of life known, and are protein-wrapped genetic material. Viruses are not complete cells and do not reproduce in food. Instead, they need a living host (like animals, plants, humans) in order to grow and reproduce. Once they have found their host, viruses can transfer from food to food, from handler to food, and from water to food. It is important to note that some viruses survive cooking or freezing. There are two viruses that are of the most concern to the food industry: Norovirus and Hepatitis A. These micro-organisms usually contaminate food through poor hygiene by food handlers, contaminated water supplies, or shellfish harvested from sewage-contaminated waters.

Hepatitis A

Hepatitis is a serious illness which causes inflammation of the liver. Hepatitis A is a communicable disease associated with many foodborne illnesses. It is particularly important to the food industry because it has an incubation period of 15-50 days. In most cases symptoms appear 2 to 6 weeks after infection. This means that a foodservice worker can be infected with the virus for a period of up to 6 weeks without showing symptoms of the illness. During this time, food can become contaminated through poor personal hygiene by food handlers. Other routes of contamination include ready-to-eat foods and vegetables washed in non-potable water, and shellfish harvested from fecal-contaminated water.

Norovirus and Norwalk Viruses

Both of these strains are members of a group called *calciviruses*. Previously known as "Norwalk-like viruses" they are associated with many outbreaks of foodborne illness. Infection with norovirus affects the stomach and intestines, causing gastroenteritis. Often mistaken for the "stomach flu", gastroenteritis is an inflammatory condition which can make people feel very ill and vomit without warning many times a day.

People working in the food industry who have norovirus are a particular risk to others. This is because the virus can be in the body fluids of infected persons from the day they start to feel ill to as long as 2 weeks after they feel better. Noroviruses are very small in size and it takes very few of them to make people sick. This micro-organism is highly contagious.

The best defence against foodborne viruses is good personal hygiene.

Parasites

Parasites are single or multi-celled, sometimes wormlike, living micro-organisms that need a host to survive. While parasites cannot grow in food, they can be passed to people through food. Perhaps the best known parasite is *Trichinella spiralis*, a naturally occurring roundworm that can be transferred to humans. Traditionally found in pigs, today *Trichinella spiralis* is more often found in wild animals, particularly bears. If not killed by thorough cooking or freezing for specified time periods, its larvae can cause trichinosis, a disease that causes painful abdominal and muscular cramps. Another parasite of note is *Anisakis simplex*, a roundworm that lives in fish. People who eat raw, marinated, or partly cooked fish may be at risk.

Protozoa are microscopic, one-celled parasites found in soil and water. Most protozoa living in the environment are not harmful. Many types of protozoa are even beneficial in the environment, improving the quality of water by eating bacteria and other particles. Some protozoa can make people sick. The most common sickness caused by protozoa is giardiasis which is caused by a one-celled parasite called *Giardia Lamblia*.

A person may get giardiasis from contaminated water, contact with a person who has the infection or through contaminated food. A person infected with giardiasis can spread the infection to other people if they do not wash their hands properly after using the toilet.

Cryptosporidiosis is a disease caused by the protozoan parasite *Cryptosporidium parvum*. Cryptosporidium can be found in soil, food, water or on surfaces contaminated by the feces of infected humans or animals. People are infected when they swallow the parasite. Food and water from unknown sources should be avoided. Ensuring foodhandlers practice good personal hygiene, thoroughly wash produce, use sanitary water sources and thoroughly cook food are the best preventative measures. Similarly, *Cyclospora* is a waterborne parasite common to tropical and subtropical areas that can be transmitted to humans via the fecal – oral route. Outbreaks have been linked to fresh fruits and vegetables. Proper cooking and freezing may help reduce the incidents of Cyclosporiasis.

Fungi

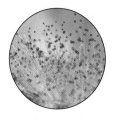

Fungi are micro-organisms that range from single-celled plants to large, multicellular organisms like mushrooms. Fungi are found in air, soil and water.

Some types of fungi are also found on skin, in the intestines of animals, and in insects. They are transferred from place to place by carriers and air currents.

Moulds

Moulds are tiny fungi that live on plants and animals, and can be carried by air, water and insects. Single mould cells are usually microscopic, but mould colonies may be seen as fuzzy growths on food. You only see part of the mould on the surface of food. Once there is visible growth, the mould has already invaded deep into the product.

Moulds are responsible for spoilage of food. Some moulds also produce toxins that can cause allergic reactions, nervous system disorders, kidney and liver damage, and chronic respiratory problems. For example, aflatoxin, produced by the moulds *Aspergillus flavus* and *Aspergillus parasticus*, can cause liver disease.

Moulds grow under a variety of conditions, on almost any food at almost any storage temperature. While most prefer warm temperatures, some can also grow at refrigerated temperatures. They also grow well in acidic foods with low water activity, and high salt or sugar content.

Freezing prevents or slows the growth of moulds but will not kill those already present in food. The toxins produced by some moulds can withstand cooking. A key food safety control to prevent illness caused by mould toxins is to throw out food with moulds that are not a natural part of that food. Check items near the mouldy food for contamination.

Yeasts

Yeasts require sugar and moisture to survive; they are often found in foods such as jellies and honey. Although most yeasts are beneficial to the food industry, some cause spoilage of food and disease in plants, animals and humans. Yeasts spoil these products by slowly eating the sugars and producing carbon dioxide gas. Contamination appears as bubbles, an alcoholic smell or taste, pink discolouration, or slime.

Seafood Toxins

To control foodborne illnesses caused by seafood, only buy fish from a reputable and certified supplier. Carefully select the kinds of fish you will serve, noting the following toxins:

Systemic Fish Toxins

Puffer fish, moray eels, and freshwater minnows contain natural toxins. Cooking may not destroy these toxins. Puffer fish should be handled and prepared by properly trained personnel.

Ciguatera Toxin

Certain species of amberjacks, barracuda and snapper may eat smaller fish that have eaten algae carrying ciguatoxin, a naturally occurring marine biotoxin. The ciguatera poisoning is caused by eating fish which, through their diet, have accumulated elevated levels of ciguatoxin. Symptoms include vomiting, itching, nausea, dizziness, hot and cold flashes, temporary blindness, hot and cold sensory reversal, and sometimes hallucinations. Any part of the fish may contain the ciguatera toxin, however, the liver, head, gonads and viscera have been reported to contain higher concentrations. Ciguatoxin is not destroyed by cooking. Purchase fish only from approved suppliers.

Scomboid Toxin (histamine)

Fish such as tuna, bluefish, marlin, bonito, mackerel, mahi-mahi, herring, and sardines have been implicated in histamine poisoning. When kept too long in the Temperature Danger Zone histamine is formed. Histamine can trigger a severe allergic reaction when consumed in high doses. Symptoms include flushing and sweating, a burning or peppery taste, nausea, and headache. Other symptoms may include facial rash, hives, edema, diarrhea, and abdominal cramps. Histamine is odourless, tasteless, and not destroyed by cooking. Fish products should only be bought from reputable suppliers.

Shellfish Toxins

Bivalve shellfish have a hinged two-part shell. They include oysters, clams, scallops, mussels and cockles. Bivalve shellfish feed by filtering microscopic plankton and marine algae from the water. This way of feeding may increase the concentration of chemicals, bacteria, viruses and biotoxins in their tissues. Marine biotoxins may accumulate to levels which cause illness or even death. Paralytic Shellfish Poisoning (PSP) and Red Tide are the most common human illness associated with shellfish in Canada. CFIA monitors harvesting areas and hundreds of sites in Atlantic Canada, Quebec and British Columbia are regularly tested for toxins. Symptoms include tingling and numbness of the lips, tongue, hands and feet, and difficulty swallowing. Severe poisoning may lead to paralysis and death in 12 hours. Marine toxins are not destroyed by cooking.

Bacteria and viruses may also accumulate in shellfish. Areas that don't meet sanitary standards are officially closed to harvesting by the CFIA. There is the potential for illness due to *Vibrio parahaemolyticus* (Vp) found in our coastal waters in summer months. Infection results in gastroenteritis which may last several days.

Only shellfish harvested from open harvest areas should be consumed. Purchase bivalve shellfish from reputable, federally approved suppliers.

Plant Toxins

The reason for the presence of natural toxins in plants is not always known. Commonly eaten plants, and foods made from plants, may contain toxins. The following have been involved in outbreaks of foodborne illness:

- Fava beans, rhubarb leaves, jimson weed and water hemlock.

- Honey from bees that have gathered nectar from mountain laurel, milk from cows that have eaten snakeroot, and jelly made from apricot kernels.

- Some varieties of mushrooms. Since poisonous and non-poisonous mushrooms often look alike, use only mushrooms that are bought from a reliable and approved source. Cooking and freezing do not destroy all plant toxins.

- Roots and shoots like kumaa, cassava and bamboo. Cassava and bamboo shoots contain a naturally occurring toxin called cyanogenic glycoside when raw or unprocessed. This can lead to exposure to hydrogen cyanide and its related toxicity. Cassava is also known as yucca, tapioca (a processed product of cassava), gaplek or manioc. Bamboo shoots, a traditional component of Asian cuisine, are sourced from the underground stems of the bamboo plant. To avoid exposure, peel and thoroughly cook all roots.

FIGURE 2.3 Major Foodborne Illnesses

Disease	Salmonellosis	Shigellosis	Listeriosis	Staphylococcal Gastroenteritis	Clostridium Perfringens Gastroenteritis
Pathogen	*Salmonella*	*Shigella*	*Listeria monocytogenes*	*Staphylococcus aureus*	*Clostridium perfringens*
Incubation Period	6-48 hrs. (usually 12-36 hrs.)	12-50 hours	Few days-3 weeks	rapid	8-22 hours
Duration of Illness	1-2 days (may last longer)	Indefinite, depends on treatment	Indefinite, depends on treatment; high fatality rates in immuno-compromised individuals	2-3 days	24 hours (may last 1-2 weeks)
Symptoms	Abdominal pain, headache, nausea, vomiting, fever, diarrhea	Diarrhea (sometimes bloody), abdominal pain, fever, vomiting, chills, lassitude, dehydration	Nausea, vomiting, diarrhea, headache, persistent fever, chills, backache, meningitis	Nausea, vomiting, abdominal cramps; in more severe cases, headache, muscle cramping, changes in blood pressure and pulse rate	Abdominal pain, diarrhea, dehydration
Source	Domestic and wild animals, humans (intestinal tract), especially as carriers	Humans (intestinal tract), flies	Soil, water, mud, humans, domestic and wild animals, fowl, damp environments	Humans (skin, hair, nose, throat, infected sores), animals	Humans (intestinal tract), animals, soil
Foods Involved	Poultry and poultry salads, meat and meat products, fish, shrimp, sliced melons, sliced tomatoes, milk, shell eggs, egg custards and sauces, and other protein foods	Salads (potato, tuna, shrimp, chicken and macaroni), lettuce, raw vegetables, milk and dairy products, poultry, moist and mixed foods	Unpasteurized milk and cheese, ice cream, raw vegetables, poultry and meats, seafood, and prepared, chilled, ready-to-eat foods	Ham and other meats, poultry, warmed-over foods, egg products, milk and dairy products, custards, potato salads, cream-filled pastries and other protein foods	Cooked meat, meat products, poultry, gravy, beans that have been cooled slowly
Spore Former	No	No	No	No	Yes
Prevention	Avoid cross-contamination, refrigerate food, thoroughly cook poultry to at least 85°C (185°F), rapidly cool cooked meats and meat products, avoid contamination from foodservice employees by practicing good personal hygiene	Avoid cross-contamination, avoid fecal contamination from foodservice employees by practicing good personal hygiene, use sanitary food and water sources, control flies, rapidly cool foods	Use only pasteurized milk and dairy products, cook foods to proper internal temperatures, avoid cross-contamination, clean and sanitize surfaces, avoid pooling water	Avoid contamination from bare hands, practice good personal hygiene, exclude foodservice employees with skin infections from food preparation, properly refrigerate food, rapidly cool prepared foods	Use careful time and temperature control in cooling and reheating cooked meat, poultry, and bean dishes and reheat products to 74°C (165°F) for at least 15 seconds within two hours
Type of Illness	Infection	Infection	Infection	Intoxication	Toxin-mediated Infection

FIGURE 2.3 Major Foodborne Illnesses

E. coli O157:H7 Enteritis	Bacillus cereus Gastroenteritis	Botulism	Campylobacteriosis	Hepatitis A	Norovirus Gastroenteritis
Escherichia coli	*Bacillus cereus*	*Clostridium botulinum*	*Campylobacter jejuni*	Hepatitis A virus (HAV)	Norwalk and Norwalk-like viral agent
2-9 days	Emetic: 1/2-6 hours Diarrheal: 6-15 hours	18-36 hours (may vary from 4 hours-8 days)	2-5 days	15-50 days (average 28-30 days)	24-48 hours (virus can remain up to 2 weeks after symptoms subside)
8 days	Emetic: Less than 24 hours Diarrheal: 24 hours	Several days-a year	7-10 days (relapses common)	Several weeks/ months; relapse may occur	24-60 hours
Diarrhea (watery, could become bloody), severe abdominal cramps and pain, vomiting, occasional low-grade fever	Emetic: Nausea and vomiting, occasional abdominal cramps and/ or diarrhea Diarrheal: Watery diarrhea, abdominal cramps, pain, nausea	Lassitude, weakness, vertigo, double vision, difficulty speaking and swallowing, constipation	Diarrhea (watery or bloody), fever, nausea, abdominal pain, headache, muscle pain	Fever, loss of appetite, nausea, vomiting, diarrhea, myalgia, malaise; jaundice, dark-coloured urine or light-coloured stools at onset	Nausea, vomiting, diarrhea, abdominal pain, headache, low-grade fever
Animals, particularly cattle, humans (intestinal tract)	Soil, dust	Soil, water	Domestic and wild animals (intestinal tract)	Humans (direct oral-faecal route)	Humans (intestinal tract)
Raw and undercooked ground beef, imported cheeses, unpasteurized milk, roast beef, dry salami, apple cider, commercial mayonnaise	Emetic: Rice products, starchy foods (potato, pasta, and cheese products), sauces, puddings, soups, casseroles, pastries, salads. Diarrheal: Meats, milk, vegetables, fish, soups	Improperly processing canned, low acid foods, garlic-in-oil products, grilled sautéed onions in butter sauce, leftover baked potatoes, stews, meat/poultry loaves	Unpasteurized milk and dairy products, poultry, pork, beef, lamb, non-chlorinated water	Uncooked foods; produce such as green onions, lettuce, and carrots; salads and sandwiches; shellfish; glazed or iced baked goods; unpasturized dairy products; and, water	Raw shellfish, raw vegetables, salads, prepared salads, water contaminated from human feces
No	Yes	Yes	No	No	No
Thoroughly cook ground beef to at least 71°C (160°F) for 15 seconds, avoid cross-contamination, avoid fecal contamination from foodservice employees by practicing good personal hygiene	Use careful time and temperature control and quick-chilling methods to cool foods, hold hot foods at 60°C (140°F) or higher, reheat leftovers to 74°C (165°F) for at least 15 seconds within 2 hours	Do not use home-canned products, use careful time and temperature control for sous vide items and all large, bulky foods, purchase garlic-and-oil mixtures in small quantities for immediate use and keep refrigerated, cook sautéed onions on request, rapidly cool leftovers	Thoroughly cook food to minimum safe internal temperatures, avoid cross-contamination	Practice good personal hygiene, avoid touching food with bare hands, exclude foodservice employees who are infected. Avoid cross-contamination, thoroughly cook food to proper internal temperatures, clean and sanitize surfaces. Vaccines are available	Obtain shellfish from approved, certified sources, avoid fecal contamination from foodservice employees by practicing good personal hygiene, thoroughly cook foods to minimum safe internal temperatures) use chlorinated water
Toxin-mediated Infection	Emetic: Intoxication Diarrheal: Toxin-mediated Infection	Intoxication	Infection	Infection	Infection

Chemical Hazards

Chemical contamination can be caused by *chemical hazards* such as pesticides, food additives and preservatives, cleaning and sanitizing supplies, plastics and toxic metals that leach through worn cookware and equipment. Lubricants used on equipment, personal care products such as hair sprays, and paints or petroleum products can also contaminate food.

Pesticides

Food safety controls include:

• Keep food covered.

• Wash all fruits and vegetables before preparation to remove residue.

• Clean and sanitize all equipment and utensils that may have come in contact with any pesticides.

• Only allow trained professionals to apply pesticides on your premises.

If you store pesticides, keep them in their original containers. If you must put them in a different container, label the new container with the contents and hazards and store them away from food, food contact surfaces and other chemicals.

Toxic Metals and Plastics

Chemical contamination can occur during cooking or storage when certain metals touch high-acid foods. Potentially toxic metals include lead, copper, brass, zinc coating, antimony and cadmium. Some foods involved in metal poisoning are sauerkraut, tomatoes, fruit gelatins, lemonade and fruit punches.

pesticides
food additives.

The following are food safety controls:

- Use only food-grade containers.

- Use metal and plastic containers or other items only for their intended use. For example, do not use refrigerator shelves that may contain cadmium as makeshift grills or to store unwrapped meat.

- Use only proper food-grade brushes on food — never wire brushes or ordinary paint brushes.

- Do not re-use single use items such as pop bottles, margarine, pickle, ice cream or muffin containers unless marked as dishwasher or microwave safe.

- Do not use enamelware. It may chip and expose the underlying metal.

- Do not allow carbonated water in soft-drink mix systems to flow back into copper water intake lines. The carbonation may leach the copper into the water used to mix drinks (*See Plumbing in Chapter 11 for ways to avoid backflow*).

- Do not use galvanized (zinc-coated) containers for preparing or storing juices, lemonade, tea or salad dressing.

- Do not use lead or lead-based products, including lead-glazed ceramics, in food preparation areas.

Chemicals Used in Food Environments

Detergents, polishes, caustics, cleaning and drying agents, and other similar products are poisonous to humans. Keep them away from food (*See Chapter 11 for more information about training employees in chemical safety*). The following are food safety controls:

- Follow label directions for storing and using chemicals.

- Use automatic dispensers to measure chemicals.

- Store chemicals in their original containers. Keep them in dry, locked cabinets or areas away from food, food contact surfaces and other chemicals that may react with them.

- If chemicals are transferred to different, smaller containers or spray bottles, each new container must be properly stored and labeled with the contents and hazards. According to Workplace Hazardous Material Information System (WHMIS), all gloves, funnels, measuring cups and other supplies used to transfer chemicals must also be labeled and stored properly.

- Never use food containers to store chemicals or chemical containers to store food. Empty chemical containers must be disposed of as the manufacturer directs.

- Food handlers who use chemicals must wash and dry their hands before returning to food preparation duties.

- Food handlers who must take medication should never do so in a food preparation or foodservice area.

- If you suspect that any food or supplies have been tampered with, label the item, safely set it away from other products and then investigate the situation. Alert your supplier and the health department.

Physical Hazards

Physical contamination results when foreign objects are accidentally introduced to foods, including dirt, hair, broken glass and crockery, nails, staples, metal fragments and other objects. Some naturally occurring objects, like small bones, pose a *physical hazard*. The following are food safety controls:

Broken glass
- Do not use glasses to scoop ice. Use only commercial food-grade plastic or metal scoops with handles.

Crockery
- Do not chill glasses or any food items in ice that will be used for drinks.

Dirt
- Do not store toothpicks or non-edible garnishes on shelves above food storage or preparation areas.

Jewelry
- Place and maintain protective shields on lights over food storage and preparation areas.

WORD SEARCH FIND THE HAZARDS

Look closely and find 15 words related to biological, chemical and physical hazards in the puzzle below.

Find the hidden words within the grid of letters.

```
E C H A I R T X P E S P
A G I K G O F A N I C E
B I U G X T T I S E D S
O T R I U H M O M R E T
T Z N E O A I J S O T I
U R R G T R T S V P E C
L R E S E C A O I S R I
I N I T I L A X X M G D
S H S E G F P B T I E E
M I S U R I V O R O N S
L C H E M I C A L S T O
T E M P E R A T U R E S
```

BACTERIA   DETERGENT   LISTERIOSIS   SPORE
BOTULISM   GLASS   NOROVIRUS   TEMPERATURE
CHEMICALS   HAIR   PATHOGENS   TOXIN
CIGUATOXIN   HISTAMINE   PESTICIDES

- Clean can openers before and after each use and replace or rotate blade as often as necessary. Watch for small shavings of paper or metal which may fall into food.

- Remove staples, nails and similar objects from boxes and crates when food is received so these materials do not later fall into the food.

- Always keep long hair tied back and wear hair nets to prevent hair from falling into food.

- Never wear false nails when preparing or serving food.

- When boning fresh fish or poultry make sure that you thoroughly check the product for small or broken bones that may have been missed.

> Closely inspect food for physical hazards during every step of the flow of food from receiving through service.

Food Allergens

In Canada, approximately 10 million people are affected by *allergies*. It is further estimated that 5-10% of the general population and 2-8% of children are allergic to a particular food. Serving food that is safe for people with food allergies is a serious responsibility for the food handler.

Adverse food reactions are clinically defined as an abnormal response to food. Adverse reactions include food intolerance, food allergies and food *anaphylaxis*. More than 600,000 Canadians (1% to 2% of the population) are at risk of anaphylaxis.

Food Intolerance: Does not involve the immune system. It causes adverse reactions to naturally occurring components of the food or food substances that involve digestion or metabolism.

Food Allergy: An abnormal response of the immune system to a food or food substance, often a protein.

Food Anaphylaxis: Severe, sometimes fatal reaction to food. Anaphylactic reactions frequently occur within minutes of ingestion, but may be delayed by up to 4 hours.

Allergens cause a chemical change in the body, resulting in various responses depending on the type of food ingested, the individual, and the amount of allergen eaten. People with asthma tend to have much more serious reactions to food allergies. Reactions could include some or all of the following:

- Itching, burning or swelling of eyes, face, lips, tongue and throat.

- Flushing of the face and body.

- Headaches/migraines.

- Itchy, stuffy, runny nose, sneezing and phlegm in the throat (rhinitis).

- Hives.

- Tightening of the throat.

- Difficulty breathing and asthma.

- Gastrointestinal symptoms including nausea, stomach cramps, indigestion, vomiting and/or diarrhea.

- Severe vomiting and/or diarrhea.

- Loss of consciousness.

- Coma or death.

DID YOU KNOW?

Some people are highly allergic and are at severe risk if they come in contact with or ingest even trace amounts of an allergen. This means that if food is even touched by an allergen it is potentially unsafe.

IN CASE OF AN ALLERGY EMERGENCY

If a customer is actually showing symptoms of an allergic reaction IT COULD BE A MATTER OF LIFE AND DEATH! If you become aware that a customer is suffering from an allergic reaction you should:

1. Inform the person in charge immediately. Call 911 or call any other number that is appropriate in your community.
2. Ask the customer what they ate.
3. Ask the customer to stay at the establishment until they are feeling better.
4. Call the local Health Unit.

There are three ways in which an allergen may enter a person's system:

- Ingesting (either eating or drinking).

- Inhalation (breathing it in).

- Skin absorption (very rare).

As with micro-organisms, we cannot tell if a food is contaminated by tasting it or smelling it. The only way to make sure a food item is not contaminated is to make sure it never comes in contact with any other food at any stage of food handling.

Cross-contamination with allergens can occur through containers, utensils, cooking surfaces, cutting boards, frying oils, coffee grinders, employee hands and any other area, equipment, or items that come in contact with food. Food handlers must understand how foods become contaminated by allergens and how to prevent it from happening. For example, the same knife used for spreading peanut butter cannot be used for cutting a chicken sandwich until cleaned and sanitized or the sandwich will become cross-contaminated with peanut butter.

Controls

Here are some practical steps to ensure that each food product contains only the ingredients that are listed.

- Prepare food that contains a known allergen last.

- Ensure regular and proper hand washing.

- Always clean and sanitize all food contact surfaces, equipment and utensils before switching to another food to avoid carry-over. (Manufacturers should always perform an allergen clean before producing another food item.)

- Always have a recipe's component ingredients and ingredient list readily available.

- Only use approved ingredients for each recipe. Do not change, substitute, or add ingredients in a recipe.

- Do not *re-work* ingredients as they may contain allergens.

- Carefully read all labels and have the ingredients of foods prepared outside your establishment available for reference. Know whether or not an item or ready-to-eat food contains allergens or may have come in contact with allergenic substances. For example, a dessert from a bakery may have been prepared in an area that uses nuts or has been deep-fried in peanut oil.

- Properly label and store foods that may contain allergenic ingredients.

Health Canada and the CFIA have jointly identified 10 food products (*See Figure 2.4*) which are primarily responsible for about 90% of severe adverse reactions in Canada: peanuts, tree nuts, soy, milk, eggs, fish, crustacea and shellfish, sesame seeds, sulfites, and wheat. Sulfites are not a true allergen but are included as a priority allergen because severe reactions include anaphylactic shock and death.

Mustard is also now listed as a priority allergen in Canada. For more information on this decision, refer to ***Mustard: A Priority Food Allergen in Canada - A Systematic Review*** at http://www.hc-sc.gc.ca/fn-an/pubs/label-etiquet/mustard-moutarde/index-eng.php

Give Customers Accurate Information

Although it is the customer's responsibility to know which foods to avoid, it is your responsibility to help them identify those foods in a restaurant, cafeteria or catered meal. Management must have a policy for passing on information to customers that is both easy to understand and to communicate.

- Clearly list ingredients and provide accurate information when requested.

- Always inform the customer of the possibility that one ingredient may come into contact with another. For example, if the same deep fryer is used for fish as well as chicken, you must make this information known to the customer.

- If in doubt, find out: IF YOU ARE NOT SURE, TELL THEM YOU ARE NOT SURE. The customer will respect your honesty and will feel confident because you put their safety first.

For more information on allergens and how to protect your customers, contact TRAINCAN, Inc. regarding their food allergy training program.

TREATMENT

There are no cures for allergies. Allergens cannot be controlled or removed from food because it is the make-up of the food itself that is problematic. Most people who experience adverse reactions are aware of the foods they can and cannot consume. Avoiding the foods to which they are allergic is the most important way to prevent allergic reactions.

FIGURE 2.4 Priority Allergen List

ALLERGEN OR SUBSTANCE CAUSING ADVERSE REACTION	INGREDIENT CATEGORIES TO BE AVOIDED	EXAMPLES OF PRODUCTS WHICH MAY CONTAIN THESE INGREDIENTS
Peanuts and peanut products **Note:** Peanut is part of the legume family but usually does not cross-react with other legumes.	All food products containing peanut and peanut derivatives such as peanut butter, peanut flakes, peanut granules, peanut flour, peanut oil. In some areas of the world, these may be named: arachis oil, goober nuts, goober peas, ground peas, ground nuts, hydrolyzed vegetable protein or plant protein (source maybe peanut), mandelonas, Nu-nuts. [1]	• Baked goods, eg., cakes, cookies, donuts, energy bars, granola bars, pastries • Cereals • Chili • Ethnic foods, eg., curries, thai sauces, egg rolls, satays, sauces, soups • Fried, breaded or battered foods containg peanut oil • Ice cream, frozen desserts and toppings, frozen yogurt, icewater treats • Icings, glazes, marzipan • Imported chocolate • Snack foods, eg., candy bars, chocolate, dried fruits, popcorn, mixed nuts • Vegetarian meat substitutes
Tree Nuts	Almonds, Brazil nuts, cashews, chestnuts, hazelnuts/filberts, hickory nuts, macadamia nuts, pecans, pine nuts (pinon, pignolias), pistachios, shea nuts, walnuts. In some areas of the world, these may be named: mandelonas, marzipan, (almond paste) Nu-Nuts, nut meats. Mixed nuts, nut butters, nut oils, nut paste, chocolate, nut spreads, Gianduja[2].	• Baked goods, eg., cakes, cereal bars, cookies, crackers, donuts, energy bars, granola bars, pastries and pies • Cereals • Ice cream, frozen desserts, sundae toppings, frozen yogurt, ice water treats • Natural flavourings and extracts, eg., smoke flavourings, barbeque sauces • Nut-flavoured coffees • Pesto • Salads • Nougat • Snack foods, eg., chips, popcorn, chocolate, candy • Main course dishes, eg., almond chicken Note: Nutmeg is a spice and coconut is a fruit. Although they are not tree nuts, they can cause allergic reactions.
Milk and milk products	All food products containing milk and milk derivatives such as "au gratin" foods, butter, butter fat, butter oil, butter milk, caseinates (ammonium, calcium, magnesium, potassium, sodium), cheese, curds, condensed milk, cottage cheese, cream, cream cheese, dry milk, evaporated milk, flavoured milk, ice cream, skim milk, sour cream, yogurt. Lactalbumin, lactoglobulin, whey, modified milk ingredients, curds, casein, hydrolyzed casein.	• Artificial butter flavour, margarine • Batter-fried foods, casseroles, frozen prepared foods • Baked goods, eg., baking mixes, breads, cakes, cereal, crackers, donuts, milk glaze on bakery products • Canned tuna, pates, processed meats, wieners • Caramel flavouring • Coated or seasoned french fries, instant potatoes, mashed potatoes, scalloped potatoes • Nougat • Custards and puddings • Dips, salad dressings, sauces, spreads • Egg replacers • Fat substitute • Flavoured coffees, malt drink mixes • Frozen desserts, sherbet, sorbet • Non-dairy food, "pareve" food, coffee whitener • Snack foods, eg., chocolate, fruit bars, candy, seasoned potato and nacho chips • Soy cheese, tofu • Soups and soup mixes
Eggs and egg containing materials	All foods containing egg and egg derivatives such as dried egg, egg nog, egg solids, egg white, egg yolk, powdered egg, egg custards and puddings, mayonnaise, meringues, soufflés. Albumin (albumen) Ovalbumin Conalbumin Ovomucin Globulin Ovomucoid Lecithin (from egg) Ovotransferrin Livetin Ovovitellin Lysozyme Vitelin	• Baked goods, eg., breads, cakes, cookies, donuts, muffins, pancakes, pastries • Baking mixes • Battered foods • Coating mixes • Creamy dressings, salad dressings • Confectionery, eg., chocolate, nougat • Egg replacers • Fat substitutes • Glaze on baked goods • Icings • Malt drink mixes • Pasta, eg., egg noodles • Sauces, eg., bearnaise, hollandaise • Soups
Fish and fish products	Anchovy, bass, blue fish, bream, carp, catfish, char, chub, cisco, cod, eel, flounder, grouper, haddock, hake, halibut, herring, mackerel, mahi-mahi, marlin, monkfish, orange roughy, perch, pickerel, pike, plaice, pollock, pompano, porgy, rockfish, salmon, sardine, shark, smelt, snapper, sole, sturgen, swordfish, tilapia, trout, tuna, turbot, white fish, whiting.Caviar, ceviche, gravad lax, imitation crab, kamaboko, lox, minced fillets, roe, sashimi, scrod, surmi.	• Antipasto • Canned spreads • Caesar salad • Dips • Ethnic foods • Gelatin • Marshmallows • Pizza topping • Salad dressings • Sauces, eg., Worcestershire • Soups • Sushi Note: Inhaled fish protein from sizzling fish has been reported to cause severe reactions in some sensitive individuals.

1 Nu-Nuts and Mandelonas are made from peanuts that have been deflavoured, reflavoured and reformed to look and taste like other tree nuts.
2 Gianduja is a creamy mixture of chocolate and chopped nuts found in premium and imported chocolate and ice cream.
Figure 2.4 is printed with permission from the Canadian Restaurant and Foodservice Association (CRFA).

FIGURE 2.4 Priority Allergen List

ALLERGEN OR SUBSTANCE CAUSING ADVERSE REACTION	INGREDIENT CATEGORIES TO BE AVOIDED	EXAMPLES OF PRODUCTS WHICH MAY CONTAIN THESE INGREDIENTS
Shellfish	**Crustacea:** Crab, clayfish (crawfish, ecrevisse), lobster (langouste, langoustine, coral, tomalley), prawns, shrimp/crevette, snails (escargot). **Mollusks:** Abalone, clams, cockle (periwinkle, sea urchin) conch, mussels, octopus, oysters, scallops, squid (calamari).Cuttlefish, seabob, seafood.	· Dips, spreads · Ethnic foods, eg., fried rice, paella, spring rolls · Fish mixtures · Garnishes · Sauces · Soups
Soy and soy products	All foods containing soy and soy derivatives such as: shoyu sauce, soy analog, soy flour, soy grits, soy milk, soy oil, soy nuts, soy sauce, soy spreads, soy sprouts. Edamame, hydrolyzed soy protein, hydrolyzed plant protein (HPP) or hydrolyzed vegetable protein (source may be soy), miso, natto, okara, soya, soja, soybean, soyabeans, soy protein (isolate, concentrate) tempeh, textured vegetable protein (source may be soy), tofu (soybean curds), yuba.	· Baked goods, eg., bread, bread crumbs, cereals, cookies · Breaded foods · Canned pasta · Canned tuna · Canned and packaged soup mixes · Cooking spray · Diet drinks, energy bars · Fried, breaded or battered foods containing soy oil · Frozen desserts, soy ice cream, soy pudding, yogurt · Lecithin · Margarine · Pizza topping · Processed meats, eg., burgers, deli, meat analogs, patties, vegetarian meat substitutes, wieners · Sauces, eg., teriyaki, Worcestershire · Snack foods, eg., candy, popcorn, candy bars · Soy cheese Note: The source of hydrolyzed (plant or vegetable) protein must be checked with the manufacturer.
Wheat and other gluten sources	Bulgur, couscous, durum wheat, enriched flour, enriched white flour, farina, flour, gluten, graham flour, high gluten flour, high protein flour, hydrolyzed wheat protein, kamut, semolina, spelt, triticale (wheat & rye hybrid), wheat bran, wheat germ, wheat malt, wheat starch, wheat pasta, white flour, whole wheat flour. **Gluten Only** Oats and oat gum, barley, barley flour, pearl barley, pot barley, rye, rye flour, rye bran, sprouted rye, malted grains, malt	· Most baked goods, eg., breads, bread crumbs, cereals, cookies · Baking mixes · Baking powder · Battered fried foods · Binders and fillers in processed meat, poultry and fish products · Candy, candy bars, snack foods · Canned soups, "thicked" soups · Malted milk, malted milk powder, malt · Beer, ale, lager, brewer's yeast · Coffee substitutes made from cereal · Gelatinized starch, modified starch · Gravy mixes · Icing sugar · Mustard, seasonings · Natural flavouring (from malt, wheat) · Sauces, eg., chutney, soy sauce · Vegetable gum, vegetable starch · Breads, baked products, cereals, cereal products, alimentary pastes (pastas) made from oats, rye, barley, or any of their products · Meat substitutes made from gluten or gluten flour or containing oats, rye, barley, or any of their products
Sesame seeds and sesame seed products	All food products containing sesame and sesame derivatives such as sesame oil, sesame flour, sesame seed paste, seeds, herbs, spices. In certain areas of the world, these may be named: tahina, tahini, benne or bene seed, benniseed, gingelly, sim sim, til, sesarmol or sesamolina.	· Baked goods, eg., breads, bread sticks, bread crumbs, crackers, melba toast, crisp breads, flat breads, cookies, nutritional snacks, granola bars, pastries · Cereals · Herbs, spices · Ethnic foods, eg., Chinese, Middle Eastern, Thai, eg., stir fry, shish kebab, stews, flavoured rice, noodles · Pates, dips and spreads, eg., humus · Marinades, gravies, sauces · Main course dishes, eg., sesame chicken · Salads, dressings and soups · Halvah, pretzels, rice cakes, bagel chips, pita chips
Sulphite (not a food allergen, but appears on the list as a result of a high incidence of sensitive individuals)	**Sulfating agents:** Potassium bisulphite, potassium metabisulphite, sodium bisulphite, sodium dithionite, sodium metabisulphite, sodium sulphite, sulfite, sulphurous acid. Sulphur dioxide.	· Alcoholic & non alcoholic wines, beers, ciders · A variety of processed foods such as frozen dough, gelatin, jams, jellies, ketchup, marmalade, mincemeat, molasses, mustard, pickles, quick meal mixes, relishes, sauces, soups, sweeteners, tomato paste, tomato pulp, tomato puree, vinegars. · Breads, cookies, crackers · Candy bars, snack foods · Coconut · Crustaceans and shellfish · Dried fruits, dried vegetables · Frozen mushrooms, frozen sliced apples · Fruit juices · Glazed fruits · Grapes · Guacamole · Prepared raw foods · Starch · Syrups

Summary

- Microbial contaminations are responsible for the majority of foodborne illnesses.

- Understanding how micro-organisms grow, reproduce, contaminate food and infect humans is the key to understanding how to prevent foodborne illnesses.

- Bacteria are of greatest concern because they are more commonly involved in foodborne illnesses than all the other micro-organisms.

- High temperatures like those reached during cooking can kill most of the bacteria.

- Spores produced by bacteria survive conditions that are normally adverse for biological hazards.

- The acronym FAT-TOM is an easy way to remember the key points to controlling growth of micro-organisms.

- Denying micro-organisms the conditions that support growth is the key to preventing foodborne illness.

- Viruses are the smallest of the microbial contaminants.

- Viruses are spread by humans. Practising good personal hygiene and minimizing hand contact with ready-to-eat foods is the most important defence against foodborne illnesses caused by viruses.

- Parasites live inside many animals that humans eat.

- Proper cooking and freezing kills parasites and are therefore critical factors in controlling foodborne illnesses caused by parasites.

- Moulds and yeasts are responsible for spoiling food. Moulds can produce toxins, which can harm us.

- Discard all foods that show signs of spoilage.

- Chemical contamination can occur as a result of cooking or storing foods in metal containers made with lead, copper, brass, zinc or other toxigenic coating. Only use food-grade containers.

- Chemical and physical contaminations make food unsafe.

- Chemicals should be properly labeled and stored away from food.

- Exercise extreme caution during receiving in order to avoid physical contamination.

- Make sure your establishment has a method of informing customers about food allergies and your employees are aware of the problem foods.

- Have an extensive ingredient list for all the foods at your establishment including ready-to-eat foods and any product received from other establishments. Never change a recipe, substitute or add ingredients.

INGREDIENT LISTS

Can be found _____ in my workplace.

Consider This....

When the health services department at a local college began to report an unusually high number of students infected by *Salmonella*, public health stepped in to investigate. A statement released by the chief medical officer of Breenhurst County Health Department identified 22 ill students as living in the same dormitory and having eaten meals at the same college cafeteria in the previous two days.

Ill students were interviewed in order to identify the source of the outbreak. Of the 22 ill students, 15 of them had eaten cantaloupe in the two days before they got sick and the remaining 7 had eaten roast beef sandwiches on the day after the cantaloupe had been served. When the cafeteria staff were questioned, officials learned that the employee preparing the cantaloupes had not cleaned the fruit before they were sliced into wedges and placed on ice in the display case. The cutting board and knife had then been used to slice some of the beef to be used for making sandwiches the next day. The beef was not immediately refrigerated after slicing.

Why was it deduced that the cantaloupe
was likely the food associated with this outbreak?

Answers can be found on page 200.

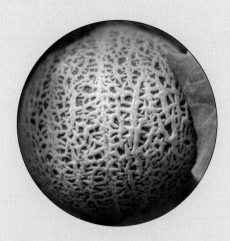

EXERCISE 2

1. **The Temperature Danger Zone for potentially hazardous foods is:**
   a. -4°C to 24°C (25°F to 75°F).
   b. 29°C to 71°C (85°F to 160°F).
   c. 22°C to 43°C (72°F to 110°F).
   d. 4°C to 60°C (40°F to 140°F).

2. **The two most important factors to control the growth of bacteria are:**
   a. Oxygen and acidity.
   b. Moisture and oxygen.
   c. Acidity and moisture.
   d. Temperature and time.

3. **The best defence against foodborne viruses is to:**
   a. Examine food carefully for spores.
   b. Use good personal hygiene.
   c. Freeze all meat during storage.
   d. Blanch all vegetables before preparation.

4. **Mould can grow:**
   a. Only on high-protein foods.
   b. Only on high-sugar foods, such as jellies and honey.
   c. On almost any food.
   d. On any foods that do not have a hard skin, casing or shell.

5. **When using pesticides you should:**
   a. Keep uncovered food in the kitchen.
   b. Throw out equipment the pesticides may have touched.
   c. Be the person to apply them.
   d. Store them away from food and other chemicals.

6. **The best tool for scooping up ice for beverages is:**
   a. A sturdy, wide-mouthed water glass.
   b. Your hands.
   c. A clean used can or jar.
   d. A commercial food-grade scoop with a handle.

7. **Allergens may enter a person's system through:**
   a. Ingestion (eating, drinking).
   b. Inhalation (breathing).
   c. Anaphylactic shock.
   d. Both a and b.

8. **If a customer reports an allergic reaction:**
   a. You should ask them what they ate.
   b. You should inform the person in charge immediately.
   c. Call emergency service.
   d. All of the above.

Answers can be found on page 198.

Supporting Good Personal Hygiene

A manager/operator or supervisor's responsibilities include setting up policies that encourage good *personal hygiene* and setting a good example with their own personal hygiene practices to avoid the contamination of food.

Cycle of transmission

There are three major parts in the cycle of transmission: food, food handler and environment. The food handler is the most important link in the cycle.

Direct transmission of foodborne disease occurs when micro-organisms transfer directly from the source to the food through ways such as touching, coughing, or sneezing directly onto the food.

ENVIRONMENT
- Work surfaces
- Utensils
- Insects
- Air

FOOD HANDLER
- Skin
- Nose
- Hair
- Hands
- Clothing

FOOD

Proper Handwashing

Train your employees to properly wash their hands and make sure that they have proper handwashing stations and supplies.

LEARNING OBJECTIVES

After completing this chapter, you should be able to:
- Describe the link between personal hygiene and foodborne illness.
- Set up basic standards for personal hygiene.
- Show support for good personal hygiene by setting an example.

TEST YOUR FOOD SAFETY IQ

1. True or False: There should be a sink designated for handwashing only in every food preparation area. (*See Handwashing Stations & Supplies page 42*)

2. True or False: Beards are exempt from hair restraint requirements. (*See Other Rules of Good Hygiene, page 45*)

3. True or False: It is acceptable to chew gum in food preparation areas. (*See Eating Areas, page 46*)

4. True or False: People can carry and spread a disease without showing any symptoms of the disease. (*See When an Employee is Ill or Injured, page 48*)

5. True or False: Gloves are a good replacement for handwashing. (*See Gloves, page 45*)

TERMS TO KNOW

Carrier: Someone who does not show any noticeable signs of being sick but carries micro-organisms that can be transferred to food or other people which can cause a foodborne illness.

Direct Transmission: The transference of micro-organisms directly from the source to the food. (eg., Touching, coughing, sneezing directly onto the food).

Finger Cot: A protective covering used to cover a properly bandaged cut or wound on a finger.

Gastrointestinal Illness: An illness relating to the stomach or intestine.

Infected Lesion: A wound or injury that is contaminated with a pathogen.

Personal Hygiene: Sanitary health habits that include keeping the body and hair clean, wearing clean clothes, and washing hands regularly.

Sanitizing Lotion: A liquid used to lower the number of micro-organisms on the surface of the skin.

Single-Use Gloves: Disposable gloves used to provide a barrier between the hands and the food they come in contact with.

HANDY HYGIENE HIGHLIGHTS

- Foodhandlers must keep fingernails short and clean.

- Always wear clean clothes, since dirty clothes can harbour pathogens.

- Never wear your work clothes when travelling to work, especially on public transport!

- Hand cuts or sores should be covered with a clean bandage and a glove or finger cot.

- Hand sanitizers and gloves do not replace handwashing!

Handwashing Stations and Supplies

There should be at at least one dedicated handwashing sink in every food preparation area (*See Figure 3.0*). Proper use of handwashing facilities is essential to personal cleanliness and to reduce the likelihood that food will become contaminated. Improper handwashing is a major contributor to outbreaks of foodborne illness. Handwashing facilities should:

- Be conveniently located for use by food handlers in the food preparation area and in areas where workers are handling cash as well as serving food.

- Be accessible for the use of workers at all times.

- Be provided with single-use soap dispensers (eg., liquid soap) and single-use hand drying devices such as paper hand towel dispensers or roll dispensers.

- Be equipped with a sign explaining proper handwashing procedures.

- Be easy to clean and maintained in a clean and sanitary manner.

- When handling or food exposure is limited, alternative handwashing facilities may be provided if approved by the regulatory authority (eg., handwashing facilities in conjunction with other plumbed services such as dishwashing sinks and/or alcohol-based hand cleansers).

FIGURE 3.0 Proper Handwashing Station

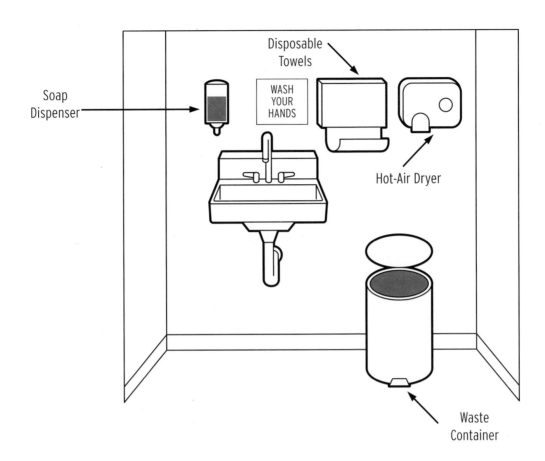

Soap Dispenser

Disposable Towels

WASH YOUR HANDS

Hot-Air Dryer

Waste Container

Hot and Cold Faucets

Each handwashing sink faucet should allow employees to mix hot and cold water to a temperature of at least 43°C (110°F). This temperature is hot enough for proper cleaning, but it will not scald.

Hand Soap

Install dispensers that allow employees to touch only the soap that is being dispensed, not the enclosed supply. Nailbrushes to clean fingernails and a sanitizing solution to soak the brushes between uses may be supplied. (Some health units discourage using nailbrushes because of the potential for misuse.)

Sanitizing Lotions

Sanitizing lotions or hand dips (liquids used to lower the number of micro-organisms on skin) may be used after handwashing, but may never be used in place of handwashing. All lotions must be stored in sealed dispensers. Train employees not to touch food or food contact equipment with bare hands until the sanitizing lotion has dried.

Single Use Paper Towels and Dryers

Hand drying equipment must be in food preparation areas so employees are not tempted to use their aprons or wiping cloths to dry their hands. Single use paper towels or roll dispensers must be provided at each hand sink.

The garbage can used for paper towels must be kept clean and set to the side. If possible, place it near the door so that employees can use the paper towel to open the door. Restrooms used by female employees must include a covered container for sanitary napkins.

Handwashing

Managers must train foodhandlers to properly wash their hands and monitor them when possible. Food handlers should thoroughly wash their hands before commencing work. The FRFSC recommends the following procedure for thorough handwashing: vigorously rub together the

FIGURE 3.1 Personal Hygiene – Handwashing

HOW TO WASH YOUR HANDS THE FOOD SAFETY WAY

1. Wet Hands

2. Apply soap

3. Vigorously scrub for at least 20 seconds

4. Rinse hands

5. Dry hands

6. Turn off water with paper towel to avoid recontamination

A waterless hand sanitizer can be applied after hand washing is complete.
These liquids/gels aid in the reduction of micro-organisms on the hands.

surfaces of the lathered hands and exposed arms for at least 20 seconds followed by a thorough rinsing with warm clean water. Some jurisdictions require 30 seconds. Attention must be given to the tips of the fingers and between all fingers. This is especially important after using the washroom (*See Figure 3.1*).

The FRFSC recommends that a nail brush and soap be used to clean underneath fingernails. Some experts don't recommend using a nail brush. If the brush is not kept in a sanitizing solution it may spread micro-organisms from one person to another. Food handlers must also wash their hands after each of the following activities:

• Using the washroom.

• Returning from a break.

THE GLOVE POLICY

In my workplace is:

_____

- Handling raw food.

- Touching their hair, face or body.

- Sneezing or coughing.

- Smoking and chewing tobacco or gum.

- Eating or drinking.

- Cleaning.

- Taking out the garbage.

- Any other activity or instance where hands may become soiled.

After washing their hands, employees should never:

- Use their aprons to dry their hands.

- Do anything that could recontaminate their hands before returning to work, such as touching their hair, sores, cuts or infected areas.

Hand Care

Hands need regular care to ensure that they don't transfer micro-organisms to food. Basic hand care includes:

- Keeping nails short and clean.

- Not wearing fingernail polish or artificial nails while handling food.

- Covering all cuts and sores with bandages and plastic gloves.

Gloves

Gloves may help keep food safe by creating a barrier between hands and food. Gloves do not replace hand-washing. Employees may use several kinds of gloves — mesh gloves for cutting, rubber gloves for dishwashing and disposable plastic gloves for food handling. Many organizations have specific policies regarding the use of gloves. Be sure to be aware of the policy in your workplace. Employees must always:

- Wash their hands before putting on gloves and when changing into a fresh pair of gloves.

- Change gloves as soon as they become soiled or torn and before beginning a different task.

- Change gloves after handling raw meat and before handling cooked or ready-to-eat foods.

- Change gloves at least every 4 hours during continual use and more frequently when necessary.

A growing number of people have a sensitivity to latex. It is important that alternatives be provided in this case. Gloves should also be available in different sizes to provide the best possible fit for each employee.

Other Rules of Good Hygiene

While personal hygiene may be a sensitive subject, it is vital to food safety. Illness can be spread by almost every part of the human body. Employees should:

- Wash their hair often and bathe daily.

- Wear clean, comfortable clothing on the job. Work clothes should be worn only on the job, not for personal use. Food handlers should put on their work clothes at the establishment.

- Wear comfortable closed-toed shoes. Never wear platform, high-heeled, absorbent-soled or open-toed shoes.

- Wear hair restraints. These are required by local, provincial or federal health legislation. Hair nets and clean hats may be used. Employees with beards should also wear beard restraints.

- Never wear jewelry. Medical alert bracelets or necklaces may be permitted. All rings, bracelets, watches and necklaces must be removed before preparing food. They are hard to keep clean and pose a safety hazard if they catch on equipment or accidentally fall into the food. Some jurisdictions allow plain wedding bands to be worn during food preparation. This should be verified with your local health unit. Many companies have rules about body piercing. In most cases, if they are visible, they must be removed, however if this is not possible they must be covered.

Tasting Food During Preparation

The safest and most sanitary way to taste food is to ladle a small amount of food into a small dish. Taste the food with a clean spoon. Remove the tasting dish and spoon from the area immediately after tasting and have them cleaned and sanitized.

Smoking Areas

Many businesses, public buildings and restaurants in Canada are smoke-free. If this is not the case in your area, set up smoking areas away from food preparation areas. Many restaurants forbid smoking inside the building.

Eating Areas

Most workplaces have a policy regarding eating and drinking in food preparation areas. Special areas should be set up for employees to consume food and drink. Medication, if required, should be stored and taken in the designated eating area – not in preparation or foodservice locations. Chewing gum should not be permitted in food preparation areas.

Dressing Areas and Storage of Personal Items

As a manager, you should provide a clean, secure area where employees can safely change and store their belongings away from food preparation areas. Dressing areas should be:

- Easily cleanable, well-ventilated and well-lit.

- Provide secure facilities for storing workers' possessions.

- Completely enclosed and provided with a lockable door, unless separate facilities are provided for each sex.

Employee Restrooms

EMPLOYEES MUST WASH HANDS BEFORE LEAVING THE RESTROOM

Properly located and equipped toilet facilities are necessary to protect equipment, facility and food from faecal contamination which may be carried by insects, hands or clothing. Toilet facilities that are kept clean and in good repair minimize opportunities for the spread of contamination. At least one toilet, or more if deemed necessary by the regulatory agency, should be provided for the use of workers in each food premise. These facilities must comply with the provisions of the National Building Code to the extent deemed necessary by the regulatory authority.

Toilet rooms should:

- Be completely enclosed and provided with a tight-fitting and self-closing door, with the exception of those washrooms which are designed for use by handicapped persons.

- Be equipped with handwash stations, have handwashing notices prominently displayed and have well-positioned waste containers.

- Have hooks outside the facility to hang aprons, white coats, etc.

- Be conveniently located and accessible to workers during all hours of operation.

- Be easily cleanable, well-ventilated and well-lit.

When an Employee is Ill or Injured

The manager or operator of a food premise should ensure that all personnel who come in contact with food are free from any symptoms of illness or communicable disease. Managers and/or supervisors are responsible for ensuring appropriate action is taken, which may include excluding that individual from activities that involve the handling of food or food contact surfaces, or authorizing the individual's absence from the work place. Employees suffering from a communicable disease have a responsibility to advise management. If they become ill or injured during a shift, they must report it immediately to a manager or supervisor.

Cuts, burns, boils, sores and *infected lesions* must be bandaged. Bandages should be clean, dry and prevent leakage from the wound. Waterproof, disposable plastic gloves or *finger cots* should be worn over bandages. Employees wearing bandages may need to be switched to tasks away from food. Employees with the following conditions should stay at home:

- Fever.

- Diarrhea.

- Upset stomach, nausea or vomiting.

- Sore throat or sinus infection.

- Coughing or sneezing.

- Dizziness.

Employees need to feel comfortable about talking with a manager or supervisor when they do not feel well because:

- People can carry and spread a disease without showing any signs of the disease.

- Even after symptoms disappear, disease-causing micro-organisms can remain in the *carrier's* body.

- Employees may hide an illness to avoid losing pay.

Summary

- Food handlers can contaminate foods at every step in its flow through the operation.

- Good personal hygiene is a critical protective measure against contamination and foodborne illness.

- Food handlers are at a high risk of contaminating food when they have been diagnosed with or show symptoms of *gastrointestinal illness*, when they have infected lesions or cuts, or when they touch anything that contaminates their hands.

- The absence of symptoms does not mean that the food handler is free from the micro-organisms that can cause illness.

- Proper handwashing is critical to preventing foodborne illnesses.

- Hands must be properly washed every time a task is interrupted, after using the washroom, after a break, before and after handling raw food, after sneezing, coughing, drinking, eating and smoking as well as anytime they are contaminated.

- Simple acts such as touching of the hair can contaminate food.

- In addition to proper handwashing, general personal hygiene is also critical. This includes having a clean uniform, bathing or showering before work, keeping nails short, not wearing any nail polish or jewelry and making sure that hair is covered when preparing food.

- Make sure all lesions are covered with clean bandages and gloves or finger cots are worn over them.

- Gloves are for *single use* and should not be washed or re-used. They should be changed every time a task is interrupted, when they are torn or when they become soiled.

- Hands must be washed before putting on gloves.

- Food handlers must be encouraged to report health problems to management before working with food.

- Managers/operators should exclude food handlers from working with or around food if they have symptoms that include fever, diarrhea, vomiting, sore throat and jaundice.

ATTENTION!

Management should model proper personal hygiene practices at all times!

Consider This....

Joe's Dairy Bar is a popular stop en route to cottage country. A family-run establishment for more than 30 years, Joe's serves its renowned burgers, shakes and soft ice cream cones to a steady stream of loyal and enthusiastic patrons. Only open during the late spring and summer months, Joe's prides itself in helping out the local community by hiring high school and college students from the nearby town.

On opening weekend, Sharon's responsibility was the soft-serve machine - from filling the hopper with mix to dispensing the ice cream into cones. It was a busy weekend; the unusually warm temperatures brought crowds of people who lined up for their first taste of Joe's for the new season. In the heat of the kitchen, Sharon began to feel unwell and wondered if her traveler's diarrhea, picked up during her vacation 2 weeks ago, was returning. Not wanting to let her co-workers down, Sharon made it through her shift but had to use the restroom several times.

Since the restroom soap dispenser had run out part way through her shift, Sharon took a few minutes at the end of her shift to refill it.

The next weekend the local public health unit called. After receiving a number of reports of severe diarrhea caused by *Shigella*, an investigation by the health unit had determined that almost all of the ill people had eaten ice cream cones from Joe's Dairy Bar during its opening weekend.

How could this outbreak have been prevented? What policies should Joe's put in place to avoid future problems?

Answers can be found on page 201.

Exercise 3

1. **Which of the following is the correct procedure for handwashing?**
   a. Use warm water, moisten hands and apply soap, rub hands for 20 - 30 seconds, rinse thoroughly, dry hands with paper towel.
   b. Use cold water, moisten hands and apply soap, rub hands for 10 - 20 seconds, rinse, dry hands with paper towel.
   c. Apply soap, rub hands, rinse, dry with cloth.
   d. Use warm water, moisten, rinse, dry with paper towel.

2. **The most important rule of foodservice personal hygiene is that employees must:**
   a. Wear gloves at all times.
   b. Completely give up smoking.
   c. Wash their hands often.
   d. See a doctor twice a year.

3. **Employees who wear disposable gloves should:**
   a. Not wash their hands before putting on gloves.
   b. Wash their hands before putting on gloves.
   c. Wash off the gloves if they become soiled with food.
   d. Apply hand lotion before putting on gloves.

4. **Handwashing stations should allow employees to:**
   a. Conveniently wash their hands when necessary.
   b. Wash and dry their hands in 10 seconds.
   c. Stand up straight while washing their hands.
   d. Use the facilities without extensive training.

5. **An employee should stay home if they suffer from:**
   a. Vomiting.
   b. Diarrhea.
   c. Fever.
   d. Any or all of the above.

6. **Which of the following items can be used to dry hands?**
   a. Apron.
   b. Single-use paper towel.
   c. A wiping cloth.
   d. All of the above.

7. **Can a food handler perform regular food preparation duties with a cut on their finger?**
   a. Yes, if they have a doctor's note to show that the cut is not contagious.
   b. Yes, if they use antiseptic between jobs.
   c. Yes, if the cut is bandaged and they wear a finger cot over the bandage.
   d. No, they should be exempt from food preparation until the cut has healed.

8. **The safest way to taste food while preparing it is to:**
   a. Taste directly from the ladle used for stirring.
   b. Have another employee hold the spoon while you taste.
   c. Use a large spoon, then rinse it so it can be used again.
   d. Ladle a small amount of food into a dish and taste it with a clean spoon.

Answers can be found on page 198.

THE FLOW OF FOOD
PART
2.0

CHAPTER 4 THERMOMETERS

TEST YOUR FOOD SAFETY

1. True or False: Data loggers are the most commonly used thermometers in foodservice. (*See Types of Thermometers, page 55*)

2. True or False: Digital thermometers should always be left in food as it cooks. (*See Figure 4.4 Thermometer Specifications, page 58*)

3. True or False: Glass or mercury thermometers can be substitutes for metal thermometers. (*See Types of Thermometers, page 53*)

4. True or False: Puncture bulk liquid packages to take the temperature reading. (*See Figure 4.3 Using Your Thermometer, page 57*)

5. True or False: Food thermometers should be accurate to 1ºC or 2ºF. (*See Types of Thermometers, page 53*)

Why are Thermometers Important?

Temperature control is the single most important aspect of food safety. In previous chapters you learned how time and temperature affect the growth of bacteria. You also learned that food cannot be exposed to the Temperature Danger Zone for excessive periods of time without the risk of foodborne illness becoming very real.

Food temperatures need to be taken:

- When food is delivered.

- When food is being stored.

- When food is thawed.

- When food is prepared.

- When food is cooked.

- When food is cooled.

- When food is on display or being held.

- When food is reheated.

It is important to take the temperature of food regularly and implement corrective actions as required. Subsequent chapters will discuss each of these actions in detail. Your thermometer is an important tool and needs to be treated with care and respect.

LEARNING OBJECTIVES

After completing this chapter, you should:

- Be able to identify the thermometers safely used in the food industry.
- Know when to use food thermometers.
- Know when and how to maintain thermometers.
- Know when and how to calibrate a thermometer.

TERMS TO KNOW

Bi-metallic Thermometer: A common food industry thermometer that measures temperature through a metal stem with a sensor.

Boiling Point Method: Boiling potable water is used to check the accuracy of thermometers. Note that the boiling point of water lowers with increased sea level.

Calibration: The process of making sure a thermometer gives accurate readings by checking it against fixed points on the temperature scale (eg., the freezing point or boiling point).

Calibration Nut: The part of a bi-metallic thermometer that is adjusted to re-set the temperature during calibration. In digital thermometers this is usually a button.

Data Logger: A unit that records air temperature at pre-set intervals and allows data to be downloaded into a software program. Some models can also take internal temperatures with a probe.

Digital Thermometer: A thermometer that provides a digital read out - sometimes referred to as a thermistor thermometer.

Dimple: An indentation on the stem of a bi-metallic thermometer that indicates how far the stem should be immersed or inserted.

Distance-to-Spot Ratio: The size of the area being evaluated by an infrared thermometer as it relates to distance.

Ice Point Method: A simple and reliable way to check the accuracy of thermometers using crushed ice and potable water.

Infrared Thermometer: A non-contact thermometer that measures surface temperature using infrared or laser technology.

Probe: The sensing area of a thermometer.

Time-Temperature Indicator (TTI): A time and temperature monitoring device that is a strip of liquid crystals that change colour when packaged contents reach an unsafe temperature.

Thermocouple: A digital reading, hand held thermometer that provides quick temperature readings through a sensor on the tip of the stem.

Types of Thermometers

Your employees need to be able to use and take care of several types of food thermometers.

Food thermometers should be able to measure internal temperatures from -18°C to 104°C (0°F to 220°F). They should be accurate to ±1°C or ±2°F. It is always best to buy thermometers from a restaurant supplier or the manufacturer. Thermometers widely available in "kitchen" stores may not be meant for industrial use, and may not hold up well in the foodservice/food retail environment. There are several common types of food thermometers, as listed below.

Thermocouple Thermometers

Thermocouples measure temperature through a sensor in the tip of the stem. When the user turns it on, the thermocouple produces a digital read-out of the temperature. This device accurately and quickly measures a range of temperatures without the need to recalibrate often. You should refer to the manufacturer's instructions for the best *calibration* method.

Always use metal food thermometers. Mercury-filled or glass thermometers may break and are *not* acceptable in a food operation.

FIGURE 4.0 Bi-metallic Stemmed

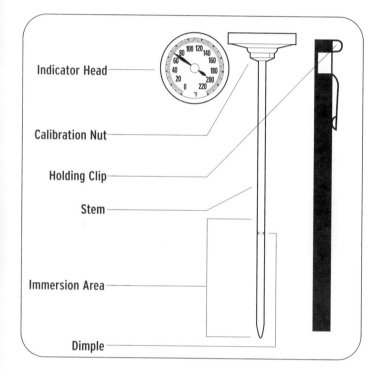

Indicator Head

Calibration Nut

Holding Clip

Stem

Immersion Area

Dimple

Bi-metallic Stemmed Thermometers

Bi-metallic stemmed thermometers (sometimes called Bitherms) are the most common type of foodservice thermometer (*See Figure 4.0*). Temperature is measured through a metal stem with a sensing area that extends from the tip to half-an-inch past the *dimple*. It is important to make sure the temperature reading has stopped before removing it from the product; otherwise, you will get an incorrect reading. Also, regular calibration is essential with this style of thermometer – rough handling, such as rolling around in a drawer or dropping it, can result in a loss of accuracy. When selecting and using a bi-metallic stemmed thermometer, remember that it should have:

- An adjustable *calibration nut*.

- Easy-to-read numerical temperature markings.

- A dimple marking the end of the sensing area (which begins at the tip).

Digital Pocket Thermometers (Thermistor)

Digital thermometers measure temperatures through a metal tip or sensing area and provide a digital readout (*See Figure 4.1*). They are especially easy to read. Thermistors have variable length stems and can be used for penetration or air readings. They can also be used for surface readings when placed between two packages. Not all digital pocket thermometers can be calibrated. Those that can usually have a button that can be depressed while the stem is immersed. Refer to the manufacturer's instructions for the best calibration method.

Time-Temperature Indicators (TTIs)

Liquid crystals in strips that change colour when packaged contents reach an unsafe temperature are called *time-temperature indicators* (TTIs). They are often used with sous-vide, MAP, or cook-chill packaging (*See page 63*).

Infrared Thermometers

Also known as non-contact thermometers, *infrared thermometers* measure surface temperatures using infrared technology. This means that you need to be careful when taking a food temperature that no other object comes between the thermometer and the product that you are monitoring. For example, if you are taking the temperature of meat sitting in a cabinet with a glass door – the reading will reflect the glass temperature unless the door is open. Likewise if the lens is dirty, or steam covered, this will prevent an accurate reading. Models designed for use in the food industry are intended to quickly and accurately identify problem areas - critical temperatures must still be verified using an internal temperature measuring thermometer. It is also important to check the manufacturer's specifications for the "*distance-to-spot ratio*", or the size of the area being measured, of an infrared thermometer. In general, the farther you are from the product, the bigger the spot size for the reading. Refer to the manufacturer's instructions for proper use, care and storage.

Data Loggers

Data loggers are devices that record temperature readings in their memory. They can download this information to a computer as part of a food safety program. These thermometers can eliminate paper temperature charts found in foodservice/ food retail operations. Temperature ranges, memory capacity and probe compatibility vary with the data logger model.

Other Food Thermometers

There are a variety of other thermometers designed for various food related applications. Some examples include candy thermometers which tend to have a higher temperature range, cappuccino thermometers that have key frothing ranges, and grill thermometers which are basically bitherms without stems.

> Use the right thermometer for the job.

FIGURE 4.1 Thermocouple Thermometers

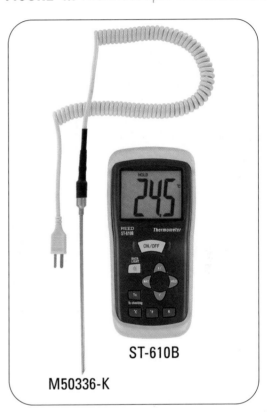

ST-610B

M50336-K

FIGURE 4.2 Calibrating Thermometers

Ice-point method

Ice-point method		
Step	**Process**	**Notes**
1.	Fill a container with crushed ice and add drinkable water.	Makes a 50/50 ice-water slush.
2.	Put the thermometer in the container, make sure the *probe* is completely submerged, wait for 30 seconds or until needle is steady.	Make sure the tip does not touch the bottom or sides of the container.
3.	Turn the nut until it reads 0°C (32°F).	

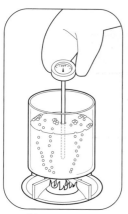

Boiling-point method

Boiling-point method		
Step	**Process**	**Notes**
1.	Boil drinkable water in a container.	
2.	Submerge the sensor into the boiling water. Wait until the needle stops.	Do not let the sensor touch the bottom or sides of the container. Protect your hands from the heat.
3.	Using a small wrench, turn the calibration nut until the thermometer reads 100°C (212°F).	

Calibrating Thermometers

Thermometers must be calibrated (adjusted) regularly to be sure readings are accurate. Check your thermometer for damage and reading accuracy at the start of every shift, and if you drop or bang it. Extreme temperature change is another example of a situation requiring recalibration.

Bi-metallic stemmed thermometers and thermistors may be calibrated by one of two methods: ice-point method or boiling-point method (*See Figure 4.2*). Thermocouples, digital pocket thermometers, and

FIGURE 4.3 Using Your Thermometer

Product	Method
Meat, Poultry, Fish	Insert the thermometer/probe directly into the thickest part of the product (usually the centre).
Soups, Stews and Large Containers	Stir the product and insert the thermometer in the centre of the batch.
Packaged Food (refrigerated and frozen)	Insert the thermometer stem or probe between two packages, being careful not to puncture them.
Milk and Other Liquids	Insert the thermometer stem or probe until at least 2 inches (5 cm) is submersed. Don't let the stem or probe touch the sides of the container.
Bulk Milk or Liquids	Fold the bag over the stem of the thermometer or probe.
Live Shellfish	Insert the thermometer stem or probe into the middle of the carton or case, between the shellfish.
Shucked Shellfish	Insert the thermometer stem or probe into the container until the sensing area is completely submersed.

infrared thermometers should be calibrated according to manufacturer's instructions. If calibration is being performed on an electronic thermometer, it is wise to use both methods. This helps to prevent inaccuracies at different temperature extremes.

The ice-point method is a safer and more reliable way to calibrate a thermometer. Thermocouples and digital pocket thermometers can be sent to a repair service for calibration and testing, but most are designed for onsite calibration.

You need to be very careful when using the boiling-point method to avoid burns. Gloves are a good idea, and exercising extreme caution is always necessary.

Reminder: The boiling point lowers about 0.6°C (1°F) for each 550 feet above sea level, so you need to adjust your thermometer accordingly.

General Guidelines for Using Food Thermometers

Thermometers need to be maintained and handled properly. Be sure to wash, rinse, sanitize and air dry thermometers between each use. Keep them protected in their case whenever possible. Bi-metallic thermometers should be stored in a cup on a shelf, rather than left to roll around in a drawer.

Thermometers need to be tested regularly. Extreme temperature changes can affect performance, as can impact – for example if the unit has been dropped. Follow the steps outlined above for calibration to ensure that your thermometer is working properly. Set up a regular calibration schedule to avoid the use of untested thermometers.

FIGURE 4.4 Thermometer Specifications

Type of Thermometer	Speed	Placement	Usage Considerations
Bi-metallic *oven safe *glass lens	1 - 2 minutes	5-6 cm (2-2.5 inches) deep in the thickest part of the food	· Can be used In roasts, soups and casseroles. · Can be placed in a food while it is cooking. · Not appropriate for thin foods. · Heat conduction of metal stem can cause false reading.
Bi-metallic *instant read *usually plastic lens	15 - 20 seconds	5-6 cm (2-2.5 inches) deep in the thickest part of the food	· Can be used in roasts, soups and casseroles. · Use to check the internal temperature of a food at the end of cooking time. · Can be calibrated. · Cannot measure thin foods unless inserted sideways. · Cannot be used in an oven when food is cooking unless it has glass lens. · Temperature is averaged along 2 -3 inches of the probe. Calibration Sleeve
Data Logger	programmed at pre-set intervals	wall mounted in a tamper proof holder	· Monitor fridge and freezer storage units. · Will do most food applications. · Check cooling times/curves. · Usually has downloadable software packages.
Digital Pocket (Thermistor)	10 seconds	at least 1 cm (1/2 inch) deep in the thickest part of the food	· Gives faster reading. · Can measure temperature in thin foods (insert horizontally). · Digital face is easy to read. · Cannot be used in an oven while food is cooking. · Waterproof units will provide maximum life.
Infrared	1 - 4 seconds	check optical ration and manufacturer specs for correct distance to food surface - there are some limitions in food use	· Surface temperature only. · Receiving and storage areas. · Suspect readings should be verified by a probe reading internal temperature.
Thermocouple *digital	5 seconds	0.5 cm (1/4 inch) deep or deeper, as needed	· Fastest. · Can quickly measure even the thinnest food. · Digital face easy to read. · Some units can be calibrated. · More costly.

Photos courtesy of Thermor Ltd.

Thermometers need to be used properly (*see Figure 4.3*). Insert the stem so that the sensing area is in the centre of the food. Do not over-insert the thermometer, and be sure to avoid bones. Wait at least 15 seconds for the reading to steady and then record the reading. Do not let the sensing area touch the bottom or sides of food containers.

Thermometers can be used to measure frozen, refrigerated, tepid and hot foods and liquids. Make sure you know what kind of thermometer you are using and its limitations. *Figure 4.4* provides an overview of different types of thermometers.

WORD SEARCH FIND THE HAZARDS

Search the following puzzle for ten word or terms related to thermometers.

Find the hidden words within the grid of letters.

```
I R J N G G Y V P I Q T E G H D U E I S
H J P O Z L H E Q O U U H V V T L I B F
O C O N D U C T I O N N H H M P F G C K
S E G C F S D N G N M N O Y M Z N J C D
H O H O S R I K B R L O X I G C J V O G
Z G A N C C A I I P U I D T Z F J Z T Y
A Q E T T R Q M Q D T T N I O P E C I C
G J T A H P M D M D Z A J B B P N S A U
O I F C P E S T E M J R M I U L T E P J
A G G T R Z N E S E N B M V V V R B W U
D C Z S I T Y A C L J I V Z M A R T T Q
Y A I C S A T K G R V L X E G Z A E Y K
A O T P Q P E I R D Q A R N O R W X M F
N K Y A J U O Z E Z I C I V G B P X I G
D C M N L D W Z I B V S H S N E C Y H Y
K H S N G O I H G S N Q L L I O N S Z D
N W O S A X G A T E T G M T D Q P W T H
U Y P W X S W G S G L O A G A G E V C J
G S H M F C N Z E G P Q P Z E A C R I I
T C H C U B B Y F R L M K S R A M Z C I
```

CALIBRATION NUT	DIMPLE	NON CONTACT	SPOT SIZE
CONDUCTION	ICE POINT	READING	STEM
DATA LOGGER	IMMERSION	SENSING AREA	TTI

Summary

- Check the temperature of food regularly and consistently.

- Ensure that thermometers are calibrated on a regular basis and checked for visible signs of damage often.

- Understand the usage of your thermometer – not every temperature monitoring device operates in the same way.

- Take care of your thermometer – keep it clean, sanitized and stored properly between each use.

- Bi-metallic stemmed thermometers are the most common type of foodservice thermometer.

- Never use mercury filled or glass thermometers in food operations.

EXERCISE 4

1. **The single most important aspect of food safety is:**
   a. Temperature control.
   b. Personal hygiene.
   c. Customer satisfaction.
   d. Both b and c.

2. **If the sensing area of a thermometer touches the bottom of a food container you should:**
   a. Perform a new reading immediately.
   b. Adjust your reading by 1°C or 2°F.
   c. Not worry about it.
   d. Wait an hour and take another reading.

3. **A thermometer should be calibrated:**
   a. After each use.
   b. If it has been dropped.
   c. After an extreme temperature change.
   d. Both b and c.

4. **The temperature of live shellfish:**
   a. Cannot be taken.
   b. Should be taken with a TTI.
   c. Can be taken by inserting the probe into the case, between the shellfish.
   d. Is not important.

5. **Thermometers should be:**
   a. Washed and dried with a clean cloth before each use.
   b. Rinsed before each use.
   c. Washed, rinsed, sanitized and air dried between each use.
   d. Wiped with a soapy cloth before each use.

6. **To measure the temperature of milk that is packaged in a soft bulk container:**
   a. Pour the milk into a bowl.
   b. Use a TTI.
   c. Poke a small hole in the container.
   d. Fold the container around the thermometer.

7. **The dimple of a thermometer:**
   a. Is the marking that indicates the depth of insertion required.
   b. Should not touch meat, poultry or fish.
   c. Can be adjusted during calibration.
   d. Is made up of liquid crystals.

8. **An infrared thermometer is best used:**
   a. For measuring surface temperatures.
   b. In dusty environments.
   c. For reading through glass containers.
   d. For verifying critical internal temperatures.

Answers can be found on page 198.

TEST YOUR FOOD SAFETY

1. True or False: Look for suppliers who allow you to inspect their trucks. (*See General Purchasing Guidelines, page 62*)

2. True or False: If a delivery arrives during a busy time, put off checking expiration dates and product temperatures until the time is more convenient. (*See General Receiving Guidelines, page 63*)

3. True or False: Shellfish shells should be open when they are received. (*See Receiving Criteria for Different Foods, page 66*)

4. True or False: Home canned products are acceptable as long as you know the supplier. (*See Receiving Criteria for Different Foods, page 68*)

5. True or False: There is no need to record a shipment if it is rejected. (*See Rejecting Shipments, page 69*)

General Purchasing Guidelines

Safe food begins with foodservice and food retail operators having the knowledge to make informed purchasing decisions. Before they buy anything, managers must find suppliers with a demonstrated, reliable commitment to operating in a sanitary manner. To enter the flow of food with confidence, choose suppliers who:

- Are reliable and get their product from a source approved by the regulatory authority having jurisdiction.

- Are inspected and are in compliance with local, provincial, and federal laws.

- Use properly refrigerated delivery trucks.

- Train their employees in sanitation, food safety and personal hygiene.

- Use protective, leak-proof, sturdy packaging.

- Work with you to schedule deliveries so goods do not arrive during busy periods.

- Cooperate with your employees when inspecting food that is delivered.

- Allow you to inspect their delivery trucks and production facilities for any signs of contamination.

LEARNING OBJECTIVES

After completing this chapter, you should be able to:

- Set up purchasing and receiving standards and procedures.
- Choose reliable suppliers.
- Design and coordinate receiving facilities and equipment.
- Purchase and inspect specific foods.
- Reject shipments.

Aseptically Packaged: A system of packaging products in sterilized containers that is followed by hermetic sealing to prevent microbiological recontamination of the sterile product.

Expiration date: Date on a package or label that shows how long the food can be safely used or kept.

Hazards: Items that may contaminate food at any time during its flow through a foodservice or food retail operation.

Lot Code: The lot code is a serialized number printed on an individual container. This serves as a reference or identifying number to track production information.

Modified Atmosphere Packaging (MAP) Foods: MAP is a packaging process by which air is removed from a food package and replaced with gases such as carbon dioxide and nitrogen.

Sous-Vide Foods: Foods processed by this method are vacuum-packaged in individual pouches, raw, partially or fully cooked and then chilled. These foods are typically cooked or reheated for a very long period of time at a very low temperature. Some health experts believe this method of cooking is dangerous because of the Time and Temperature Principle.

UHT Foods: These foods are heat treated at very high temperatures (minimum 140°C/ 284°F for at least 5 seconds) for a short time to kill micro-organisms that can cause illness.

Vacuum-Packaged Foods: Vacuum packaging is the process of removing air from around a food product sealed in a package.

General Receiving Guidelines

All food products received at a food premise should be properly packaged and labeled according to requirements outlined in the *Food and Drugs Act* and the *Consumer Packaging and Labeling Act.* The following points are guidelines to help develop your operation's receiving protocols.

- Provide the necessary facilities and equipment for receiving.

- Set delivery times so goods do not arrive during busy periods.

- Receive only one shipment at a time.

- Assign well-trained employees to receive all goods.

- Inspect delivery trucks for evidence of possible contaminants and accurate temperature controls for refrigerated and frozen foods.

- Use data loggers to record air temperatures throughout the shipping and receiving process.

- Goods must arrive in sanitary conditions and be handled properly.

- Inspect supplies right away, check expiration dates and use-by dates.

- Use thermometers to measure product temperatures.

- Sample all bulk items and individual packages within cases.

- Log in acceptable goods.

- Use appropriate logs to track the receiving and/or rejection of goods. Logs should include a section for recording temperature data.

- Reject unacceptable goods or contact a supervisor immediately to do so. Be sure to note the reasons for rejection in the log.

- Remove *hazards* such as staples, nails and other fasteners before unpacking boxes and crates.

- Move all food into proper storage right away.

Facilities and Equipment

When setting up your receiving area, be sure that it is:

- Clean, well-lit, pest-free and supplied with copies of receiving rules.

- Equipped with sanitized carts, dollies, hand trucks and containers and has areas for washing, drying, wrapping and rewrapping supplies.

> Remember, for a product to be traceable and legal under federal law, it must be properly labeled. In case of a recall, *lot coding* is essential as it allows a specific item to be traced and recalled.

Receiving Criteria for Different Foods

Meats – Lamb, Beef and Pork

Temperature: Receive at 4°C (40°) or lower.

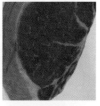
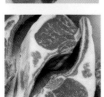
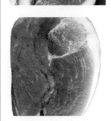

Accept Criteria:
Beef: Bright red and moist.
Lamb: Light red.
Pork: White fat with pink lean portions.

Reject Criteria:
Colour: Brown or greenish, purple blotches or black, white or greenish spots.
Texture: Slimy, sticky or dry.

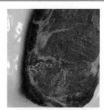

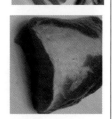

Other Criteria: Meats should only be bought from suppliers with a HACCP system in place. Suppliers should also be approved by the regulatory authority having jurisdiction. The meat should have a Canadian inspection stamp and its grade should be indicated. There are 13 meat grades – 90% being Canada A, AA, AAA or Canada prime. All other grades are grouped as utility beef. If the meat is purchased from the United States it must display a USDA inspection stamp.

Poultry

Temperature: Receive at 4°C (40°F) or lower.

Accept Criteria:
No discolouration.
Texture: Firm.
Package: Crushed self-draining ice.

Reject Criteria:
Colour: Purplish or greenish colour or green discolouration around the neck, darkened wing tips. **Texture:** Stickiness under wings and around joints, soft flabby flesh.
Odour: Abnormal odour.

Other Criteria: Should only be bought from suppliers approved by the regulatory authority having jurisdiction. It should have a Canadian inspection stamp. The container should have the poultry grade inscribed (Canada A, Utility or C).

Fresh Shellfish (such as Clams, Mussels and Oysters) Crustacea (such as Lobsters, Shrimp and Crabs)

Temperature: Receive at 4°C (40°F) or lower.

Accept Criteria:
Odour: No strong odour.
Shells: Closed and unbroken, hard and heavy for lobster. Received alive.

Reject Criteria:
Odour: Strong fishy smell.
Shells: Opened shells indicate the shellfish are dead. **Tail:** Fails to curl up when lobster is picked up.

Other Criteria: Invoice receipts and lot coding must be retained to allow tracking of unlabeled products. Shellstock identification tags must be kept on file by the source supplier for 90 days.

Fresh Fish

Temperature: Receive at 4°C (40°F) or lower.

Accept Criteria:
Bright red gills, bright shiny skin. **Eyes:** Bright, clear and full. **Texture:** Flesh and belly are firm. **Package:** Crushed self-draining ice.

Reject Criteria:
Gray or gray-green gills. **Eyes:** Sunken, cloudy or red-bordered eyes. **Texture:** Dry gills, flesh is soft and leaves an imprint when touched. **Odour:** Strong fishy or ammonia odour.

Other Criteria: Fish intended for raw consumption (including sushi fish and sashimi) can be received frozen. Be sure to ensure that the supplier has frozen the fish to a temperature of -35°C (-31°F) or below for 15 hours in a blast freezer or to a temperature of -20°C (-4°F) for 7 days in a freezer. This is required to ensure parasitic destruction.

Shell Eggs

Temperature: Receive at 4°C (40°F) or lower.

Accept Criteria:
Clean and uncracked.
Odour: None.
Condition: Firm, high yolks that are not easy to break and whites that cling to the yolk.

Reject Criteria:
Dirty, cracked.

Other Criteria: Should only be bought from suppliers approved by the regulatory authority having jurisdiction. Should have a best-before date. Buy only a one or two week supply. Buy only government inspected Grade A or B eggs. All egg products must be pasteurized.

Dairy Products – Milk and Milk Products

Temperature: Receive at 4°C (40°F) or lower.

Accept Criteria:
Only pasteurized milk. All milk products must be pasteurized.

Reject Criteria:
Unpasteurized milk. Milk products made from unpasteurized milk.

Fresh Produce

Accept Criteria:
Clean, whole and appears fresh, bright colour.

Reject Criteria:
Signs of mould, insect infestation, wilted, discoloured, unpleasant odour. Signs of bruising or excessive brown spots.

Frozen Foods

Temperature: Receive frozen at -18°C (0°F) or lower.

Accept Criteria:
Package intact.

Reject Criteria:
Fluid or frozen liquid on the package. Large ice crystals on the food. Damaged package.

Other Criteria: Ice cream can be received at -14°C to -12°C (7°F to 10°F). Due to composition, some products do not maintain an internal temperature of -18°C (0°F) – for example some baked goods. Check with suppliers for specifications.

Refrigerated Foods

Including ready-to-eat foods and other pre-cooked foods.
Temperature: Receive at 4°C (40°F) or lower.

Accept Criteria:
Package intact.

Reject Criteria:
Fluid or liquid on the package. Damaged packaged. Past use-by date. Discoloured, slime, unpleasant odour.

Canned Foods

Accept Criteria:
Can and seal in good condition.

Reject Criteria:
Swelling, leakage, rusting, dents, missing or unreadable label.

Other Criteria: Milky or foamy foods with an odour should be discarded. Never accept any home canned foods – the risk of botulism is too great.

Modified Atmosphere Products (MAP), Vacuum Packed, Sous-vide Packaged Foods, Aseptically Packaged and UHT Foods.

Temperature: Refrigerated - received at 4°C (40°F) or lower. Frozen – received frozen at -18°C (0°F) or lower.

Accept Criteria:
Packaging intact and in good condition. Expiry or best-before date has not passed.

Reject Criteria:
Expired. Damaged packaging (signs of discolouration, bubbles). Missing or unreadable labels.

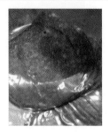

Other Criteria: Ultra-pasteurized foods include milk products and fruit juices in cartons that have been heat-treated to kill disease-causing micro-organisms. Foods labeled *UHT* have been ultra-pasteurized (heat treated at a minimum temperature of 140°C/284°F for at least 5 seconds), then *aseptically packaged* (hermetically sealed). UHT products must be refrigerated at 4°C (40°F) or lower after opening.

Hot Foods

Temperature: Receive at 60°C (140°F) or higher.

Accept Criteria:
Appropriate containers that can maintain the temperatures.

Reject Criteria:
Temperature lower than 60°C (140°F).

Dry Goods

Temperature: Receive at room temperature.

Accept Criteria:
Package intact and in good condition.

Reject Criteria:
Signs of insect infestation, mould or slimy appearance. Damaged packages, holes, puncture or tears. Water or excess moisture.

Rejecting Shipments

Your employees should know what to do when a shipment does not meet the standards outlined in your food safety system.

If it is necessary to reject a shipment:

- Keep the unacceptable food separate from your other food and supplies.

- Tell the delivery person the exact problem with the food. Use your purchase agreement and documented standards to back up your case.

- Do not throw it out or let the delivery person remove it until a signed adjustment or credit slip is in hand.

- Record the incident in the log, including the food involved, the carton number if appropriate, the standard not met and the type of adjustment made.

Summary

- All food and food ingredients must be obtained from reputable suppliers who follow good food safety procedures.

- All meat suppliers should have a HACCP program in place and be approved by the regulatory authority having jurisdiction.

- Inspect delivery trucks for conditions that might allow potential contamination between food and non-food products.

- All foods must be properly packaged and labeled in case of food recall.

- Reject all foods that do not meet the receiving requirements.

- Properly store items right away.

- Check the temperatures of all refrigerated and frozen items with sanitized, properly calibrated thermometers.

Consider This....

August 14 was a hot summer day and Catherine, the new assistant manager, was in charge of receiving the day's deliveries at White Oaks Nursing Home. Ed, who was normally in charge of receiving, was on vacation. Through bad luck or bad timing, the delivery of the frozen food products arrived during the lunch hour, followed immediately by the delivery of fresh produce and then by the delivery of specialty deli products from a local supplier. The deli delivery person made an off-handed remark as he was unloading the delivery that the refrigeration unit in his truck was having a hard time in the summer heat; Catherine didn't pay much attention because she was so busy and he always seemed to be complaining about something.

Catherine rushed to put the frozen foods into the freezer before they started to thaw. The tops on the carrots were starting to wilt by the time she got all the produce into the refrigerator. Luckily, the deli delivery was smaller, so it didn't take much more time to put it in the refrigerator. Catherine realized she had been so busy with the other deliveries that she hadn't taken the time to do a thorough check of the deli delivery, but she knew the local supplier had a good reputation so she wasn't worried.

What was done incorrectly? What could be the possible result?

Answers can be found on page 201.

EXERCISE 5

1. **A reliable supplier is one who will:**
   a. Follow regulatory requirements.
   b. Always provide the lowest price.
   c. Vary the time deliveries are made every week.
   d. Provide give-aways with each new order.

2. **When a shipment of food arrives, employees should:**
   a. Put everything away and inspect it later.
   b. Inspect only the potentially hazardous foods.
   c. Inspect all foods right away before storing them.
   d. Stack goods neatly on the dock and inspect them within 12 hours.

3. **Fresh fish should:**
   a. Be received at 7°C (45°F).
   b. Have soft flesh and dry gills when received.
   c. Be packaged in self draining ice.
   d. Both b and c.

4. **Reject any poultry that has:**
   a. A product temperature lower than 4°C (40°F).
   b. Green or purple blotches.
   c. An inspection stamp.
   d. Been packed in self-draining crushed ice.

5. **The temperature of shell eggs at receiving should be:**
   a. -4°C (25°F).
   b. 4°C (40°F).
   c. 12.8°C (55°F).
   d. 60°C (140°F).

6. **Ultra-pasteurized foods:**
   a. Have been heat treated to kill disease-causing micro-organisms.
   b. Should not be accepted if labels are missing.
   c. Include milk products and fruit juices.
   d. All of the above.

7. **If a supplier offers you a good deal on home-canned tomatoes:**
   a. Take it, but wash off the cans.
   b. Reject it, but see if the supplier has home-canned green beans.
   c. Reject it, or any other offer for home-canned foods.
   d. Take it, but chill the tomatoes to 15.6°C (60°F).

8. **If it is necessary to reject a shipment:**
   a. Call the health department.
   b. Temporarily store the unacceptable shipment.
   c. Obtain a signed credit slip from your delivery person.
   d. Do not record any information about this shipment.

Answers can be found on page 198.

TEST YOUR FOOD SAFETY

1. True or False: Wash fruit and vegetables before storing. (*See Fresh Produce, page 78*)

2. True or False: Material Safety Data Sheets are used to log temperatures in food storage areas. (*See Chemical Storage, page 79*)

3. True or False: Use your storage freezer to cool food before refrigerating it. (*See Freezer Storage, page 76*)

4. True or False: The warmest area in a refrigerator is near the door. (*See Cold Storage, page 74*)

5. True or False: Store raw ground meat below raw chicken. (*See Refrigerated Storage, page 75*)

General Storage Guidelines

Product shelf-life depends on packaging, storage area temperature and humidity, and on the type of food. Foods, such as dairy products, meats, poultry, eggs, fresh fruits and vegetables, will spoil rapidly if not stored at proper temperatures as evidenced by off odours, off flavors, off colour, and/or soft texture. As micro-organisms grow, they produce acids or toxins. Remember though, that food may be spoiled without showing any detectable signs. Following proper storage guidelines will keep your customers safe and save you money by reducing the amount of food that you have to discard!

- Provide the necessary facilities and equipment for storing food safely.

- Train your employees to monitor each kind of food while it is in storage.

- Keep food out of the Temperature Danger Zone: 4°C to 60°C (40°F to 140°F).

- Designate separate cold and *dry storage* areas for employee's personal food items.

- Ensure that all food products and ingredients are accurately and appropriately labeled with one of the following: date received; expiration (use-by) date; date prepared; or, the date it should be discarded.

- Establish a schedule to monitor in-stock items.

- Rotate stock on a regular basis use the *First In, First Out* (FIFO) method. On each package, write either the date an item was received or when it was stored after preparation. Shelve new supplies behind old, so the old are used first. Regularly check use-by dates to ensure the *shelf life* has not expired.

LEARNING OBJECTIVES

After completing this chapter, you should be able to:

- Set up storage standards and procedures.
- Provide storage equipment and facilities.
- Use the different types of storage facilities appropriately.
- Store foods safely.

Corrective Action: Action taken to correct an error or lapse in safe food-handling or HACCP procedures (*See Chapter 8*).

Dry Storage: The holding of non perishable food items at 50 to 60 percent humidity and between 10°C and 21°C (50°F and 70°F).

First In First Out (FIFO): A method of stock rotation in which new supplies are shelved behind old supplies, so the old are used first.

Food-Grade Container: A container that will not transfer harmful substances to the food it is holding.

Material Safety Data Sheet (MSDS): A sheet that lists data about a substance such as the common and scientific names of chemicals, potential physical and health hazards, toxicity and reactivity, and directions for safe handling.

Shelf Life: Recommended period of time during which a material may be stored and remain suitable for use.

- Discard all food that has passed its expiration date.

- Measure and record storage area and stored food temperatures regularly, as part of your monitoring or HACCP system (HACCP will be discussed in detail in *Chapters 8, 9* and *10*). Be sure to use the right thermometer for the job.

- Take *corrective action* each time a food item has been time or temperature abused, when it has passed its expiration date or when a storage area is at the wrong temperature.

- If an item is transferred from its original packaging or container, the new container must be clean, sanitized, and labeled with the name of the product and its use-by date. Use only *food-grade containers*.

- Keep unauthorized persons out of storage areas.

- Keep all storage areas clean and dry. Clean up all spills and leaks, and remove dirty packaging and other trash immediately.

Cold Storage

Refrigerators, deep chilling units and freezers are your main tools for keeping potentially hazardous foods cold enough to prevent bacteria from growing. To keep your cold storage units effective:

- Use storage units for storage only (*See Chapter 7 for cooling techniques*).

- Monitor food temperatures on a regular schedule.

- Avoid overloading, which taxes the cooling unit and cuts down air circulation.

- Keep the unit doors shut as much as possible. Only open them for short time periods.

FIGURE 6.0 Proper Refrigeration Storage

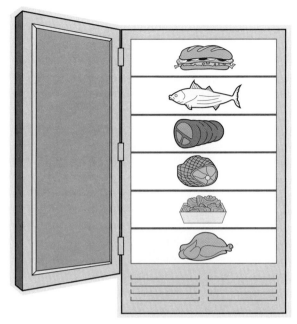

– Cooked and ready-to-eat foods

– Raw fish

– Raw unground beef

– Raw pork, ham, bacon and sausage

– Raw ground beef and ground pork

– Raw poultry

- Always place thermometers in the warmest area (usually by the door) of each unit and monitor them closely. In addition you could place a thermometer in the coldest area (usually at the back). Some units also include a read-out panel outside the unit so you can check the inside temperature without opening the door.

Refrigerated Storage

Use refrigerators to keep foods at an internal product temperature of 4°C (40°F), or less, for short time periods. This includes foods that have been prepared and cooled for service. Remember - refrigeration slows the growth of many micro-organisms.

- Store cooked and ready-to-eat foods above raw foods to avoid cross-contamination (*See Figure 6.0*).

- When storing raw foods, place on drip-proof trays and use the top-to-bottom order. The order shown in *Figure 6.0* is based on end-cooked internal temperatures (*See Chapter 7 for final cooking temperatures*).

- Health Canada recommends that ready-to-eat, potentially hazardous food prepared and not consumed within 2-3 days should be discarded or frozen. However, shelf life guidelines for specific foods are available from local health units. It is recommended that you follow these suggestions.

FIGURE 6.1 Proper Dry Storage

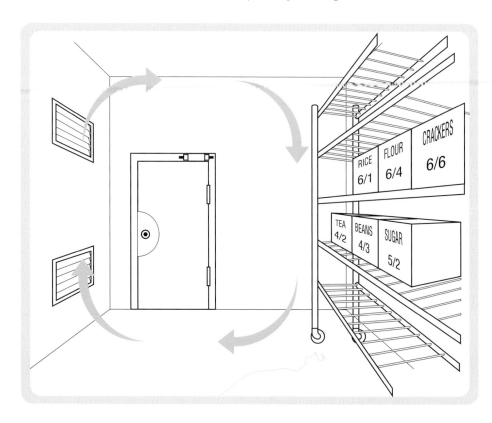

- Never line the shelves. It reduces air circulation necessary for proper cooling.

- Ideally, use two refrigerators: one for meat, poultry, fish, and dairy products and another for fruits and vegetables. Another possibility is to use one unit for raw foods and one for cooked foods.

- In retail grocery operations, ensure that refrigerated display cases are not filled above the manufacturers specified fill line.

- If doors are not practical, use cooler curtains or plastic insulating strips in walk-in refrigerators.

Freezer Storage

Use freezer units only to store already chilled or frozen foods at a unit temperature of -18°C (0°F) or lower. Thawing and refreezing damages food quality. More importantly, food that has been thawed and refrozen is more likely to have been exposed to conditions that support bacterial growth.

- Move frozen foods from receiving to freezer storage as soon as they are received and inspected.

- Regularly check unit and food temperatures. Foods that may be damaged by long freezing include hamburger, mackerel, salmon, bluegill, turkey, pork, creamed foods, sauces, custards, gravies and puddings.

- Regularly defrost units. Move frozen foods to another freezer during defrosting.

- Never refreeze thawed food until after it has been thoroughly cooked.

Dry Storage

Keep packages of dried fruits and vegetables, cereals and other grain products, sugar, flour and rice intact and dry. These foods may be stored for long time periods, but water and high humidity may cause bacterial growth. The expiration date of each item should be checked.

- Store dry foods at least 15cm (6 inches) off the floor in their original packages or in tightly closed airtight containers and out of sunlight (*See Figure 6.1*). Shelving should be at least 5 cm (2 inches) from the walls to allow for access and permit easier visual access.

- Storage area temperatures should be 10°C to 21°C (50°F to 70°F) with a relative humidity of 50 to 60 percent. High humidity may cause dry food to draw in moisture, resulting in caking, stale product and bacterial growth. Canned goods may also rust, leading to leaky cans. If high humidity is a problem, try a dehumidifier.

Dry storage areas must be:

- Well-ventilated and pest-free.

- Cleanable.

- Located in a clean and dry location. Keep dry food out of direct sunlight.

- An environment which minimizes the deterioration of stored materials.

- Protected from contamination during storage.

Storing Specific Foods

Your food safety system should include standards for storing each kind of food. The following list indicates the recommended requirements for different types of foods.

Meat

Storage Temperature: 4°C (40°F) or lower.
Freeze at: -18°C (0°F).

Note: Meats should be wrapped in airtight packaging for both refrigeration and freezing. They should be stored in the coldest section of the unit.

Poultry

Storage Temperature: 4°C (40°F) or lower.
Freeze at: -18°C (0°F).

Note: Store poultry in the coldest section of the unit. All frozen poultry should be wrapped airtight. Fresh refrigerated parts and whole poultry should be used within one to two days. Raw chicken received packed in ice can be stored as is or on beds or chests of self-draining ice.

Fish and Shellfish

Storage Temperature: 4°C (40°F) or lower.
Freeze at: -18°C (0°F) or lower.

Note: Whole fish delivered on crushed or flaked ice can be stored for three days. Beds or chests of ice must be self-draining. If fish is not received on ice it must be used within 48 hours. Fresh fillets should be kept in airtight, moisture proof wrappings. Fish meant to be eaten raw (Sushi fish or sashimi) must be frozen before being served. If not received frozen, fish intended for raw consumption should be stored at -20°C (-4°F) or lower for 7 days in a freezer or at -35°C (-31°F) or lower in a blast freezer for 15 hours. Live shellfish should be stored in their original containers. Frozen fish should be stored in airtight, moisture-proof wrappings.

If fish are maintained live:

- The water in which they are kept must be clean and aerated.

- Saltwater fish must be kept in salt water.

- Tanks must be clean and dead fish discarded. Identify optimal cleaning schedules and length of time to keep specific species with your supplier.

Shell Eggs

Storage Temperature: 4°C (40°F) or lower.

Note: Use FIFO. Take out only as many eggs as you need for immediate use. Liquid egg products should be stored in their original container at 4°C (40°F) or lower. Dried egg products should be stored in their original container in a cool, dry place away from light, but should be refrigerated after opening.

Dairy Products

Storage Temperature: 4°C (40°F) or lower.
Freeze at: Ice Cream at -14°C to -12°C
(7°F to 10°F).

Note: Keep packages tightly covered and away from foods with strong odours. Do not keep past the expiration date.

Fresh Produce

Storage Temperature: varies depending on product.

Note: Whole raw fruits and vegetables and cut raw vegetables received packed on ice can be stored in that ice. Beds or chests of ice must be self-draining. Regularly change the ice. Do not wash fruits and vegetables before storage.

EVALUATE YOUR STORAGE AREAS:

Canned and Dry Goods

Store at room temperature.

Note: Keep store rooms dry and humidity low. Flour, cereal and grain products should be stored in airtight well labeled containers above the floor. Check packages regularly for insect or rodent damage.

MAP, Vacuum and Sous-vide Packaged Foods

Store these products at manufacturer recommended temperatures.

Note: Discard packages that are torn or past their expiration date.

Aseptic and UHT Foods

Store unopened product at room temperature.

Note: Products should be refrigerated at 4°C (40°F) after they are opened.

Chemical Storage

To prevent possible cross-contamination with food, cleaning supplies and other chemicals should be stored:

- In locked rooms or cabinets away from food preparation and food storage areas.

- In original containers or in sturdy containers labeled with the contents and their hazards.

- Near *material safety data sheets* (MSDSs). These are written descriptions of the contents, hazards and handling procedures for chemicals and products containing chemicals. They are required by WHMIS and may be required by local regulations therefore they need to be readily available (*See Chapter 12*).

Never use empty chemical containers to store food and never put chemicals in used food containers.

Facilities and Equipment

Food must be kept out of the Temperature Danger Zone of 4°C to 60°C (40°F to 140°F) and safe from all sources of contamination. To control the temperature in storage areas, each area should be equipped with a hanging or built-in thermometer for measuring the ambient (surrounding) temperature. These thermometers should be accurate to 1°C (±2°F). Below are some general guidelines to help you plan storage facilities.

- Let air circulate around food. Provide enough slatted shelves in storerooms, refrigerators and freezers so packages do not have to be stacked on the floor, on top of each other, or against walls.

- Store food in original packaging as long as the packaging is clean, dry and intact. Never reuse old wrappings or containers.

- Repackage food in leak-proof, pest-proof, non-absorbent, sanitary, food-grade containers with tight-fitting lids.

- Store food only in proper storage areas. Never use locker rooms, restrooms, furnace rooms, hallways, stairwells or garbage rooms for storage.

- Keep food away from sewer and water lines, drains and condensation dripping from pipes or ceilings.

- Clean and sanitize all utensils and equipment, such as carts, dollies and delivery vehicles regularly.

Summary

The key to keeping food safe during storage is to keep it out of the Temperature Danger Zone where harmful micro-organisms can grow and reproduce.

- All hazardous and perishable foods must be refrigerated at an internal temperature of 4°C (40°F) or lower.

- Frozen foods should be stored at temperatures of -18°C (0°F) or lower.

- Do not transfer hot foods directly to the refrigerator — this will raise the ambient temperature of the fridge and its contents.

- Do not overload the storage units or line the shelves. Overloading interferes with the air circulation and therefore affects the temperature inside the unit.

- Always store ready-to-eat and cooked foods above raw foods.

- Store food in leak-proof, pest-proof, non-absorbent, sanitary containers with tight-fitting lids.

- Practice FIFO.

- Shelve new supplies according to their expiration dates.

- Discard food that has passed its expiration date.

REMEMBER: DO NOT TAKE CHANCES WITH FOOD. WHEN IN DOUBT, THROW IT OUT!

Consider This....

At 2:00 p.m. on August 14, the food service employees at White Oaks
Nursing Home were cleaning up after lunch and beginning to prepare dinner.
Pete, a kitchen assistant, put the still-hot container of leftover vegetable soup in the
refrigerator to cool. He noticed that the refrigerator did not feel quite as cool as
normal, but he knew that Catherine had been busy over the lunch hour putting away
the day's deliveries (see Consider This... in Chapter 5). He also realized that he had
forgotten to clear off some of the shelves to make space for the deliveries, but he was
happy to see that Catherine had found some space for the fresh produce on the bottom
shelf below the packages of chicken that were thawing for that night's dinner,
and a spot for the deli products next to the door.

What storage errors were made? What foods are at risk?

Answers can be found on page 202.

EXERCISE 6

1. **Locker rooms, restrooms, furnace rooms and stairwells are:**
   a. Unacceptable as food storage areas.
   b. Acceptable food storage areas for less than three days.
   c. Acceptable food storage areas if kept clean.
   d. Unacceptable food storage areas, but a hallway may be used.

2. **Under the FIFO method, foods are used:**
   a. In relation to size.
   b. In the order in which they were received.
   c. By selecting the freshest foods first.
   d. By the cost of the food.

3. **If stored foods have passed their expiration date:**
   a. Freeze the food for later use.
   b. Cook and serve the food at once.
   c. Discard the food.
   d. Leave it on the shelf for later use.

4. **Shelves in a refrigerator should be:**
   a. Lined with aluminum foil.
   b. Slatted.
   c. Heavily loaded for maximum use.
   d. Covered in plastic wrap.

5. **If you have hot food that you want to refrigerate:**
   a. Cool it, then refrigerate it.
   b. Put it in the refrigerator to cool.
   c. First cool it in the freezer.
   d. Leave it out on the stove overnight.

6. **While you are defrosting your freezer, put the frozen food in:**
   a. The refrigerator.
   b. Another freezer.
   c. A microwave to thaw.
   d. The sink.

7. **Which one of the following should you do when handling shell eggs?**
   a. Store them at a unit temperature of 16°C (60°F).
   b. Wash them before putting them into the refrigerator.
   c. Crack a number of them into a large bowl for later use.
   d. Take out only as many as you need for immediate use.

8. **Frozen raw fish should be stored:**
   a. Unwrapped.
   b. At -1°C (30°F) for long-term thawing.
   c. Wrapped in airtight and moisture-proof wrapping.
   d. Near the freezer door.

Answers can be found on page 198.

TEST YOUR FOOD SAFETY

1. True or False: Thawing food at room temperature is safe. (*See Thawing Food Safely, page 85*)

2. True or False: Recipes should specify end product internal temperature. (*See Cooking, page 89*)

3. True or False: In a buffet style service, new food can be mixed with old food. (*See Holding, page 91*)

4. True or False: Prepare meat and poultry salads 48 hours before serving them. (*See Salads and Sandwiches Containing Potentially Hazardous Foods, page 87*)

5. True or False: Batters and breadings containing eggs are reusable if refrigerated. (*See Batters and Breadings, page 88*)

Time-Temperature Principle

Time-temperature abuse is one of the biggest contributing factors to foodborne illness outbreaks. Time-temperature abuse occurs any time potentially hazardous food is exposed to the Temperature Danger Zone (TDZ) of 4° C to 60° C (40° F to 140° F). Within this warm temperature range disease-causing micro-organisms quickly grow and multiply. Micro-organisms grow fastest in the middle of the Temperature Danger Zone, between 21° C and 52° C (70° F and 125° F).

Combined with temperature, time plays an integral role in food safety. The longer food remains in the Temperature Danger Zone, the greater the risk of foodborne illness. Micro-organisms multiply exponentially, doubling every 10 to 20 minutes. Closely monitor and reduce the amount of time food spends in the TDZ throughout the flow of food to avoid the growth of disease causing micro-organisms. Foods are most at risk during preparation and service. As foods are received, thawed, cooked, held, served, cooled and reheated, they pass through the Temperature Danger Zone several times. Keep in mind that although temperature abuse may be only for a short period of time at each stage, the total accumulated time may be enough to cause foodborne illness. Food must not spend more than a maximum total of four hours in the Temperature Danger Zone throughout the process of preparing the food. Some jurisdictions enforce a more stringent requirement, insisting food must not spend more than a maximum of two hours in the Temperature Danger Zone. Please check with your local health unit.

LEARNING OBJECTIVES

After completing this chapter, you should be able to keep food safe throughout:

- Thawing.
- Preparing.
- Cooking.
- Holding.
- Serving.
- Cooling.
- Reheating.

TERMS TO KNOW

Blast Chiller: A unit that chills food from 60°C (140°F) to 2°C (36°F) in 90 minutes or less.

Cold-Holding Equipment: Equipment specifically designed to keep cold foods at temperatures of 4°C (40°F) or less.

Discard Time: The time at which food must be thrown out.

Hot Holding Equipment: Equipment specifically designed to hold foods at temperatures of 60°C (140°F) or above.

Ice Wand: A plastic paddle filled with water and frozen.

Ice-Water Bath: A method of cooling food in which a container holding hot food is placed inside a larger container of ice water. The ice surrounding the hot food container disperses the heat quickly.

Minimum Internal Temperature: The required cooking temperature that the internal portion of food must meet in order to sufficiently reduce the number of micro-organisms that might be present.

One-Stage Cooling: A process used for cooling food prepared at room temperature from 20°C (68°F) to 4°C (40°F) or less in four hours.

Pooled Eggs: The practice of combining several cracked eggs in a common container.

Potable Water: Water that is safe to drink or to use as an ingredient in food.

Sneeze Guard: A food shield placed in a direct line between food on display and the mouth/nose of a person of average height.

Time-Temperature Abuse: Temperature abuse has occurred when any potentially hazardous food is exposed to the Temperature Danger Zone of 4°C to 60°C (40°F to 140°F) for any amount of time.

Two-Stage Cooling: A process used to cool hot foods in two stages.

Preventing Cross-Contamination

Each time food is handled, it runs the risk of cross-contamination from other food and food contact surfaces such as human hands, cutting boards and utensils.

- Keep all ready-to-eat foods separate from raw foods.

- Prepare raw meat, fish and poultry in areas separate from fresh produce and ready-to-eat foods.

- Assign specific equipment (cutting boards, utensils and containers) to each type of food product. For example, use one set of cutting boards and utensils for poultry, another for beef, and a third for produce.

- Use utensils and other equipment as much as possible when handling food - instead of hands.

- Clean and sanitize all utensils, work surfaces and equipment that touch food after each use, when changing food and when equipment is in continual use.

KEEP HOT FOOD HOT AND COLD FOOD COLD!

- Make sure cloths or towels used for wiping spills are not used for any other purpose.

- Make sure your employees practice proper hand washing at all times.

Thawing Food Safely

As foods thaw, they move through the Temperature Danger Zone. This is a perfect time for pathogenic micro-organisms hiding in the food to begin to multiply. There are four approved ways to thaw food safely:

1. In a refrigerator at 4°C (40°F) or lower.

- Store raw foods on the lowest shelves to prevent them from dripping or splashing on other foods.

- Allow a day or more for large items, such as turkeys and roasts, to thaw.

2. Completely submerged under running potable water at a temperature of 21°C (70°F) or lower. The product should be thawed within two hours, then prepped and cooked immediately.

- Use a large cleaned and sanitized sink that is used only for thawing.

- Use a stream of water strong enough to wash off loose particles of skin or dirt. Do not let the water splash on other food or food contact surfaces.

- Remove the food from the sink as soon as it is thawed. Sanitize the sink and all utensils used in thawing.

3. As part of the cooking process. This method works well with vegetables, seafood (such as shrimp), hamburger patties, pie shells and similar foods but not with large items. Allow longer than normal cooking time to account for the additional thawing time. The product must still reach minimum, safe internal cooking temperatures.

4. In a microwave. Use this method only if the food will be cooked immediately, whether in other cooking equipment or finished immediately in the microwave. This method is not effective for large items.

Potable Water

Cooking

Microwave Oven

Preparing Food for Cooking

Detailed recipes, time and temperature controls, and sanitary procedures are the keys to food safety.

- Use properly cleaned and sanitized utensils and practice good personal hygiene.

- Use recipes that specify fat content, size and thickness of each portion. This helps predict cooking time.

- Refrigerate foods before preparation and any time preparation is interrupted.

- Prepare small batches of food no farther in advance than necessary. Return them to the refrigerator before cooking or serving.

- Use sanitized cutting boards and knives to avoid cross-contamination.

- Wash fruits and vegetables in sinks used only for food preparation.

Meat, Fish and Poultry

The source of most cross-contamination in an operation is raw meat, poultry and seafood. Great care should be taken to avoid cross-contamination.

- Take out only as much product as you can prepare at one time.

- Put raw meats back into storage as quickly as possible or cook them as soon as possible. Store them in the right place to avoid cross-contamination.

- Use clean and sanitized work areas, cutting boards, knives and utensils.

Outline the standard prep time for a potentially hazardous food in your operation:

_____

_____

Eggs and Egg-Based Mixtures

To prepare eggs safely:

- Do not pool eggs if they will not be used immediately. *Pooled eggs* are eggs that have been cracked open and combined together in a container.

- Do not stack egg trays near the griddle.

- Do not allow shells to touch or mix with egg contents. Shells are a hazardous substance and may contaminate food.

- Do not use processing equipment that grinds entire eggs and separates the shells.

- Use pasteurized shell eggs or egg product in all recipes in which eggs are not cooked or cannot be cooked to 63°C (145°F) or higher. This includes meringues and mousses, Caesar salad dressings, hollandaise and bernaise sauces, egg nog and mayonnaise.

- Use pasteurized eggs in all recipes that are served to high risk populations such as the elderly, pregnant women, infants and other diners with weakened immune systems.

- Use clean and sanitized bowls, whisks, blenders and other utensils for each new order or batch.

Salads and Sandwiches Containing Potentially Hazardous Foods

Salads and sandwiches containing meat, poultry, eggs or fish require careful handling. Since these foods are not typically cooked after preparation, there is no chance of killing micro-organisms introduced during preparation. Therefore, extreme care must be taken during preparation to keep these foods safe.

- Use properly cleaned and sanitized utensils and practice good personal hygiene.

- Prepare pasta, meat, poultry, egg and fish salads less than 24 hours before service.

- Make sure leftover proteins, like meat and poultry, have been properly cooked, held, cooled, and stored before adding them to a salad or sandwich.

- Chill all sandwich and salad ingredients (including bread) to 4°C (40°F) or lower before making the meal.

- Wash all vegetables and fruits. Blanch items such as celery and carrots.

- Use commercially made mayonnaise, not homemade.

Fresh Fruit and Vegetables

To reduce the risk of illness caused by fresh produce, follow these guidelines:

- Store fresh cut fruits and vegetables at 4°C (40°F) or lower.

- Discard any rotten fruits or vegetables. Bacteria can thrive in damaged areas. Clean and sanitize your knife after cutting these areas to prevent cross-contamination to the rest of the fruit.

- Thoroughly wash all fruits and vegetables under running potable water to remove dirt and other contaminants before cutting, cooking, or combining with other ingredients. It is advisable to separate each leaf for washing in the case of greens such as leeks, spinach or lettuce. Improperly washed fresh fruits and vegetables can become contaminated during cutting.

- Make sure that fresh fruit and vegetables do not come in contact with surfaces exposed to raw meat, fish, poultry, eggs, and cooked or ready to eat food.

- Melons, including cantaloupes, are particularly susceptible to contamination as their skin is rough and netted. Although whole melons may be stored at room temperature, refrigerate cut melon at 4°C (40°F) or lower in a clean, sanitized container.

- Avoid serving fresh raw seed sprouts to young children, the elderly, or people with weakened immune systems.

- Clean and sanitize all utensils and food contact surfaces that come in contact with fresh fruits and vegetables.

Stuffings

Stuffing poses a hazard. It usually contains potentially hazardous food, such as eggs, pork or oysters, that need to be fully cooked to minimum safe internal temperatures. It also acts as insulation, which prevents heat from reaching the centre of the meat or poultry. When cooking stuffed foods made entirely, or in part, of potentially hazardous foods, you must cook the meat until a thermometer inserted into the centre of the stuffing reaches a temperature of 74°C (165°F) or more for at least 15 seconds.

For maximum safety, separately cook stuffing to a minimum internal temperature of 74°C (165°F) for at least 15 seconds. If the cooked stuffing is not used immediately, it should be cooled and then refrigerated (*See Cooling Procedures later in this chapter*).

Batters and Breadings

Many of the foods cooked in batter or breading, such as poultry, fish and shellfish, are potentially hazardous. Batters made with eggs are also potentially hazardous. Used as stuffings, batters and breadings may insulate the food they cover and prevent complete cooking. To avoid this hazard, consider using commercially made battered and breaded items. Many pre-prepared frozen items can also be cooked frozen.

If you make and use your own batters and breadings, you should:

- Use pasteurized eggs, rather than shell eggs.

- Prepare batter in small batches.

- Refrigerate the ingredients for batters and breadings, as well as the items to be coated.

Potentially hazardous, hot foods must be held at an internal temperature of 60°C (140°F) or higher.

FIGURE 7.0 Time-Temperature Control Chart

The temperatures in the chart below come from the Canadian Food Retail and Food Services Regulation and Code (FRFSRC), Health Canada and the Canadian Food Inspection Agency. Recommended temperatures may vary depending on the regulations in each province and the way that food is cooked. Consult with your local Public Health Inspector for more information. A column has been provided for you to enter the temperature specifications in your jurisdiction.

Item	Temperature Requirement	Temperature Requirement In My Area
Poultry (Whole)	Internal temperature of 85°C (185°F) for 15 seconds	
Poultry (Parts and Ground)	Internal temperature of 74°C (165°F) for 15 seconds	
Stuffing in Poultry	Internal temperature of 74°C (165°F) for 15 seconds	
Food mixtures containing Poultry, Eggs, Meat, Fish or other potentially hazardous foods.	Cook to an internal temperature of 74°C (165°F) for at least 15 seconds.	
Reheating	Reheat to 74°C (165°F) for at least 15 seconds	
Pork	Cook to an internal temperature of 71°C (160°F) for at least 15 seconds	
Ground Meat (chopped, ground, flaked or minced beef, pork or fish)	Cook to 71°C (160°F) for at least 15 seconds	
Fish	Cook to 70°C (158°F) for at least 15 seconds	
Lamb, Veal, Beef (pieces and whole cuts) Medium	Cook to an internal temperature of 71°C (160°F) for at least 15 seconds	
Lamb, Veal, Beef (pieces and whole cuts) Medium-Rare	Cook to an internal temperature of 63°C (145°F) for at least 15 seconds	
Eggs	Cook to 63°C (145°F) for 15 seconds	

• Do not reuse batter in which items have been dipped.

Cooking

Handling foods safely prior to cooking is very important. While cooking food to the *minimum internal temperature* is the only way to kill micro-organisms, it does not destroy spores or toxins that micro-organisms create.

The minimum internal temperatures at which micro-organisms are destroyed varies depending upon the food. The minimum internal temperatures must be reached and held for the specified time. Use sanitized, properly calibrated thermometers to measure the temperatures.

Recipe instructions for cooking should specify cooking times and end product internal temperatures. Employees should:

• Cook foods to higher than their minimum safe internal temperatures if their quality will not be compromised.

• Measure food temperatures with a thermometer, accurate to ±1°C or ±2°F. Never rely on a "best guess," "experience," or equipment (such as oven) settings.

• Measure internal food temperatures in several places. Clean and sanitize thermometers before and after each use (*See General Guidelines for Using Thermometers in Chapter 4*).

- Always cook to completion – do not partially cook a product, stop, and finish at a later time.

- Avoid overloading cooking surfaces and ovens. The temperature of the unit may drop or foods may spill on each other.

- Allow the temperature of cooking equipment to return to required temperatures between batches.

- Correctly taste foods (*See Tasting Food During Preparation in Chapter 3*).

NOTE: Potentially hazardous food cooked or reheated in microwaves must be rotated and stirred throughout midway during cooking to compensate for uneven distribution of heat, and allowed to stand for a minimum of 2 minutes after cooking to obtain temperature equilibrium.

Holding

General Holding Guidelines

- Make only small batches. Breaded, fried and baked foods should be held only for very short time periods.

- For hot buffet service, be sure that individual holding compartments are not overfilled.

- Regularly stir held foods and measure their temperatures with a thermocouple or bi-metallic stemmed thermometer every two hours. Do not rely on the thermostat setting on the holding equipment. This measures the temperature of the equipment, not of the food. Record temperatures in a log.

- Use covered holding pans and provide long-handled spoons or tongs so hands do not touch the food. Place

THE REQUIRED COOKING AND HOLDING TEMPERATURES OF POULTRY IN MY WORKPLACE ARE:

_____

spoons and tongs in the food with their handles pointed toward the user or store these utensils in drinkable running water.

- Use properly cleaned and sanitized utensils and practice good personal hygiene.

- **Never** mix new food with old food.

- **Never** mix raw food with cooked food.

Holding Hot Food

Hot holding equipment includes steam tables, double boilers, bain maries, heated cabinets and chafing dishes.

To protect food during hot holding, you should:

- Only use hot holding equipment that can keep food at the proper temperature.

- Measure the internal temperature of food using a thermometer every two hours. Record them in a log.

- Discard hot foods after two hours if they have not been held at or above 60°C (140°F).

- **Never** use hot holding equipment to cook or reheat food. Most hot holding equipment does not pass food through the Temperature Danger Zone quickly enough to ensure safety.

- Stir foods at regular intervals to distribute heat evenly.

Holding Cold Food

Cold cooked and raw foods must also be kept safe from temperature abuse and contamination. *Cold holding equipment* includes refrigerated food bars, iced displays, refrigerated sandwich rails and insulated carriers. To provide control during holding, you should:

- Use only cold holding equipment that can keep foods at 4°C (40°F) or lower.

- Measure food temperatures every two hours. Record them in a log.

- Never hold ready-to-eat cold foods directly on ice. Put the foods in pans or on plates. Be sure ice used to surround chilled foods drains away from the food. Drip pans should be sanitized after each use.

Holding Food Without Equipment

Ready-to-eat or potentially hazardous foods intended for immediate consumption may be displayed or held for service at room temperature for short periods of time. Without temperature controls, foods must be:

- Handled with close attention to safe food handling practices during preparation, cooking, and/or cooling to prevent contamination.

- Labeled with the time it was removed from temperature control and with the *discard time* (the time at which food must be thrown out).

- Sold, served and discarded within 2 hours.

Room temperature holding is a risky practice because foods are exposed to the Temperature Danger Zone. The **total time** that the product is in the danger zone must be limited to 2 hours. Check with your local public health authority for specific requirements for your area.

Cooling

Food that will not be served right away should be cooled as quickly as possible to prevent micro-organisms from growing. Improper cooling has consistently been identified as a leading factor in foodborne illness. The FRFSC recommends two different cooling processes – one for cooling after cooking and another for cooling from room temperature.

Cooling After Cooking

Food must be cooled to 4°C (40°F) or lower after cooking or hot holding. The FRFSC recommends cooling in two stages:

1. From 60°C (140°F) to 20°C (68°F) or less in two hours.

2. From 20°C (68°F) to 4°C (40°F) or less in four hours for a total of 6 hours.

Remember – this is a *two-stage cooling* process. The rationale is based on the principle that, while micro-organisms grow well in the Temperature Danger Zone, the **ideal** temperature range for pathogenic growth is 60°C (140°F) to 20°C (68°F). Food must pass through this temperature range as quickly as possible.

If food does not reach 20°C (68°F) or less in two hours, it must be discarded or reheated properly (*See Reheating later in this chapter for guidelines*).

Cooling From Room Temperature

A *one-stage cooling* process is used when potentially hazardous foods are prepared at room temperature and then kept refrigerated until service. During this process, foods should be cooled from 20°C (68°F) to 4°C (40°F) or less in four hours.

Safe Methods for Cooling Food

Large food items take longer to cool. By reducing the mass and volume of an item, cooling time is decreased. This means that pathogens have less time to grow and multiply.

To reduce the quantity or size of the food you are cooling, divide large batches into several smaller ones, or cut large items into smaller pieces. Thick food, such as chili and stew, should be cooled in pans with a product depth of no

FIGURE 7.1 Cooling Foods

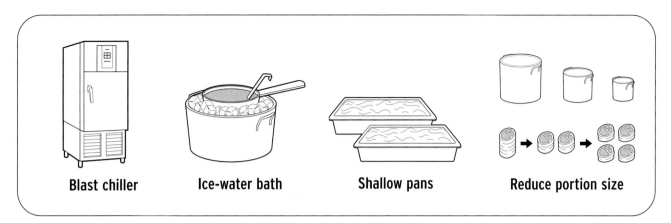

| Blast chiller | Ice-water bath | Shallow pans | Reduce portion size |

more than 5 cm (2 inches).   Thinner liquids such as broth or soup, may be cooled in pans with a product depth of no more than 7.5 cm (3 inches).

Place the smaller amounts in pre-chilled stainless steel pans. Stainless steel transfers heat from food faster than plastic, and a shallow depth allows heat to disperse faster than a deep one.

Use one of the following methods as shown in *Figure 7.1* and to the right, to move food through the Temperature Danger Zone quickly and safely:

- Use *ice-water baths.* Place the smaller containers into larger pans of ice. Stir foods as they cool – this distributes the heat evenly and foods cool more quickly.

- Use a *blast chiller,* quick-chill unit, tumbler chiller or cold-jacketed kettle.

- Stir with a clean and sanitized *ice wand.* These are plastic paddles filled with water and frozen. Stirring food with cold paddles cools food more quickly.

Ice Wand

> Never use storage refrigerators or freezers to cool hot foods. Hot foods above 20°C (68°F) can raise the temperature of the unit and endanger the other foods stored there.

How to Store Cooling Foods

Loosely cover pans to maintain airflow. Place the pans on the upper shelves of a refrigerator to cool further. Pans should be placed to allow air to circulate around them. Some health departments require pans to be covered at all times - check with your local authority.

FIGURE 7.2 Proper Serving

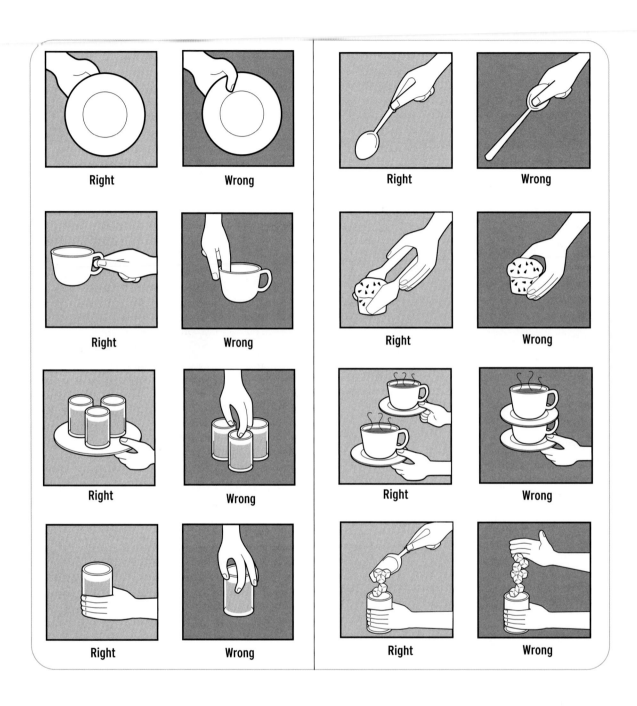

Train employees to monitor the time and temperature of cooling food. If food is not cooled within the required times and to the required temperatures, take corrective action by reheating to 74°C (165° F) within 2 hours. Record the cooling times required for each type of food and add these times to your recipes and flowcharts.

Reheating

Even when foods are cooked and cooled safely they can become cross contaminated. The reheating process is an ideal time for pathogenic bacterial growth.

To reheat food safely:

- Reheat all previously cooked food to an internal temperature of at least 74°C (165°F) for at least 15 seconds within two hours. If the food cannot be reheated within two hours, discard it.

- Reheat food in small batches to shorten reheating time.

- **Ready-to-eat** food taken from a commercially processed, hermetically sealed container or from an intact package from a certified HACCP system run processing plant must be reheated (often called rethermalized) to 60°C (140°F) or higher.

- Use cooking ranges, ovens, steamers and microwaves to reheat food.

- **Never** use hot holding equipment to reheat food because it is not designed to reach and maintain the necessary temperatures. Transfer reheated food to holding equipment only when the food is at 74°C (165°F).

- Record the reheating times for each type of food and add these times to your recipes and flowcharts.

- **Reheat food only once.** Each time a food is heated and cooled, it goes through the Temperature Danger Zone giving pathogens time to grow and multiply. Since this time-temperature factor is cumulative, each pass through the temperature danger zone reduces the lifespan of the food and increases the chance that problems will occur.

Serving

Once food has been properly cooked, food continues to be at risk of contamination during service. Managers must set up serving procedures to help employees safeguard both food and customers.

Stagger employee assignments so that an employee does not serve food, set tables, and clear dirty dishes during a single shift. Then, train staff to serve food safely (*See Figure 7.2.*):

- Practice good personal hygiene. Be neat and clean with hair pulled back. Servers should avoid touching their hair, face or other body parts.

- Use properly cleaned and sanitized utensils.

- Use plastic or metal tongs or scoops to get ice — never use glass that may break in the ice.

- **Never** touch the food contact areas of glasses, cups, plates and tableware.

- **Never** stack cups or bowls before serving them — the bottom of one will touch the rim of the one below it and possibly contaminate it.

- Avoid stacking plates to carry several of them at one time — hands may touch the food.

- Hold flatware and utensils by the handle. Store flatware so servers can easily grasp the handle rather than the food contact surface.

- Wash hands often. Especially before handling place settings, food contact surfaces or food after clearing tables or bussing dirty dishes.

LABEL PROPERLY COOLED AND STORED FOODS WITH THE DATE AND TIME THEY WERE PREPARED. CHECK WITH YOUR LOCAL HEALTH UNIT FOR SHELF LIFE GUIDELINES FOR YOUR AREA.

Self Service Areas

The self-service areas such as buffets and food bars can be easily contaminated because patrons serve themselves. In order to keep food safe during this kind of service, managers/operators should:

• Assign a staff member trained in food safety procedures to closely monitor the service.

• Assign an employee to replenish food-bar items using safe food handling practices.

• Clearly label all food items.

• Protect food display with *sneeze guards* or food shields.

• Maintain proper food temperatures. Keep hot food hot and cold food cold.

• Make sure customers use only fresh plates. Post signs or assign a staff member to prohibit the use of soiled plates or flatware in self-service areas.

• Provide long handled serving utensils in each container.

TEN RULES of Safe Food Handling

This list is in the order of the flow of food.

1. Require strict personal hygiene from all employees.

2. Identify all potentially hazardous foods on your menu and write out your food handling procedures. Make these written procedures part of employee training, everyday tasks and regular self-inspection.

3. Obtain foods and other supplies from reputable, approved sources.

4. Observe the rules for time and temperature and for preventing cross-contamination in storing and handling food prepared in advance of service.

5. Keep raw products separate from ready-to-eat foods.

6. Avoid cross-contamination of raw and ready-to-eat foods from hands, equipment and utensils. Clean and sanitize food contact surfaces and equipment before and after every use, when a task is changed, after an interruption, and at least every four hours during continual use.

7. Cook or heat process food to above the recommended minimum temperature.

8. Keep hot foods hot and cold foods cold. Hold foods at 60°C (140°F) or higher, or at 4°C (40°F) or lower.

9. Chill cooked food to 4°C (40°F) within the required time.

10. Reheat food to an internal temperature of at least 74°C (165°F) for at least 15 seconds within two hours.

Summary

- The two leading causes of foodborne illness are time-temperature abuse and cross-contamination.

- Food must be cooled to 4° C (40° F) or lower as quickly as possible. From 60° C (140° F) to 20° C (68° F) within two hours and from 20° C (68° F) to 4° C (40° F) within four hours.

- Prepare raw meats, fish and poultry in separate areas from produce or cooked food to prevent cross-contamination.

- Assign specific equipment to specific tasks.

- Clean and sanitize everything that comes into contact with food.

- Thaw food properly in the refrigerator, under running water, in a microwave or as part of the cooking process.

- Cook foods to the recommended temperatures and hold for the recommended time. Monitor the temperatures using accurately calibrated, cleaned and sanitized thermometers. Keep a detailed temperature log.

- Cool foods rapidly and properly before storing.

- Make sure food is held at 60°C (140°F) or higher using the right equipment.

- Reheat foods to 74°C (165°F) for at least 15 seconds within two hours.

- Discard food if there is evidence of time-temperature abuse.

- Make sure servers practice good personal hygiene.

- Train employees to avoid cross-contamination when handling utensils, service items and tableware.

Consider This....

Miss Lockhart's Grade 4 class was learning about Chinese New Year.
To add interest for her students, Miss Lockhart asked the owner of a nearby
Chinese restaurant to come in to the classroom to talk about traditional Chinese
New Year celebrations and to bring some foods for the students to sample. The students
tasted some foods that they had never tried before and some that were more
familiar to them including chicken fried rice.

To make chicken fried rice, the students were told, rice was cooked the
previous day, cooled at room temperature and then refrigerated. On the morning of
the classroom visit, the rice was pan-fried in oil with pieces of cooked chicken. The
restaurant owner had then transferred the fried rice and the other foods to large serving
dishes and transported them to the school for the students to sample.

Later that day, not long after the owner of the Chinese restaurant left, several
of the students who had eaten the chicken fried rice vomited and showed other
signs of foodborne illness. Health officials determined that the students
were made ill by *Bacillus cereus* emetic toxin.

*What errors were made in preparing and storing
the food for the students?*

Answers can be found on page 203.

EXERCISE 7

1. **Which one of the following is required for safe food handling?**
   a. Store hot foods at 4°C (40°F) or higher.
   b. Mix raw food with ready-to-eat food.
   c. Clean and sanitize food contact surfaces only at the end of the day.
   d. Cook food to at least the recommended internal temperature for the recommended amount of time.

2. **If you must prepare a large batch of ham sandwiches for later service, you should:**
   a. Make them all at one time, then refrigerate.
   b. Make them all at one time, then cover and leave them on the counter.
   c. Make several at a time, then cover and refrigerate them.
   d. Make several at a time, then cover and leave them on the counter.

3. **Which one of the following would you do if you were preparing a recipe using eggs that are not cooked to 63°C (145°F)?**
   a. Use pasteurized eggs.
   b. Completely drop the menu item, even if it is your most popular.
   c. Use only Grade A eggs.
   d. Chill the shell eggs to 4°C(40°F) before using.

4. **Which one of the following is the correct way to cook a stuffed turkey?**
   a. Cook the stuffing and the turkey together to 20°C (68°F).
   b. Separately cook the stuffing to 63°C (145°F).
   c. Separately cook the stuffing to 74°C (165°F).
   d. Cook the stuffing and the turkey together to 63°C (145°F).

5. **A hot potentially hazardous food should be held at:**
   a. 20°C (68°F).
   b. 50°C (122°F).
   c. 60°C (140°F).
   d. 74°C (165°F).

6. **Which one of the following procedures should employees do when serving?**
   a. Use bare hands to touch cooked food or food that will not be cooked.
   b. Touch the food contact or mouth-contact parts of dishes and utensils.
   c. Stack cups or bowls before serving them.
   d. Use plastic or metal tongs or scoops to get ice.

7. **Large amounts of thick food, such as chili, should be cooled in shallow pans with a product depth no greater than:**
   a. 5 cm (2 inches).
   b. 7.5 cm (3 inches).
   c. 10 cm (4 inches).
   d. 12.5 cm (5 inches).

8. **A tray of roasted vegetable sandwiches is displayed at room temperature for one hour, then placed in the refrigerator and cooled to 4°C (40°F). The sandwiches are then put back on display at room temperature for two hours. The food should be:**
   a. Returned to the refrigerator and cooled again to 4°C (40°F).
   b. Discarded as it has been exposed to the Temperature Danger Zone for more than 2 hours.
   c. Kept on display for another hour before being discarded.
   d. Kept on display for another hour before being cooled again to 4°C (40°F).

Answers can be found on page 198.

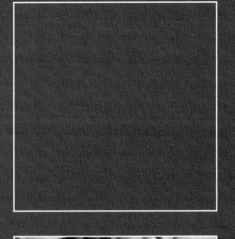

DEVELOPING A FOOD SAFETY SYSTEM

PART
3.0

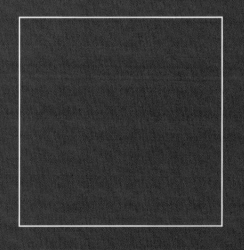

TEST YOUR FOOD SAFETY

1. True or False: In a HACCP system, only complicated recipes require flowcharts. (*See Conduct a Hazard Analysis, page 104*)

2. True or False: Receiving is a Critical Control Point (CCP) for all foods. (*See Identify CCPs, page 107*)

3. True or False: Only managers can run a HACCP program. (*See Adapting Your HACCP Plan, page 111*)

4. True or False: Job descriptions should include skills required to complete specific HACCP related tasks. (*See HAACP Training, page 111*)

5. True or False: HACCP is a food safety system designed to keep food safe. (*See What is HACCP?, page 102*)

What is HACCP?

Hazard Analysis Critical Control Point (HACCP) is a system that helps you to identify and assess the biological, chemical and physical hazards, and other *risks* associated with your food establishment. It is a tool which focuses on preventing foodborne illness by establishing controls and monitoring all procedures in the flow of food.

To be successful, a HACCP system requires a written plan that is specific to each operation. Implementing the plan requires the commitment and dedication of owners, executives, managers and employees.

Common HACCP Terms

Hazard: Any agent or condition with the potential to cause an adverse health reaction. Hazards include:

1. Micro-organisms that can grow during preparation, storage, and/or holding.

2. Micro-organisms or toxins that can survive heating.

3. Chemicals that can contaminate food or food contact surfaces.

4. Physical objects that accidentally enter food.

Hazard Analysis: The process of identifying and evaluating potential hazards associated with foods in order to decide which foods must be addressed in a HACCP plan.

LEARNING OBJECTIVES

After completing this chapter, you should be able to:

- Describe the main principles of a HACCP system.
- Assess food safety hazards.
- Identify Critical Control Points (CCPs).
- Set up Critical Limits as minimum and maximum standards for CCPs.

- Take corrective actions.
- Set up a record keeping system.
- Verify that your system is working.
- Manage a HACCP system.

Control Point (CP): Any step in the flow of food where a physical, chemical or biological hazard can be controlled.

Critical Control Point (CCP): A point, step or procedure where you can intervene to prevent, control or eliminate the growth of micro-organisms before the food is served to customers.

Critical Limit: Minimum and maximum limits that the CCP must meet in order to prevent, eliminate, or reduce a hazard to an acceptable limit.

Dry Lab: The recording of data without actually measuring it.

Hazard: Any agent or condition with the potential to cause an adverse health reaction.

Hazard Analysis: The process of identifying and evaluating potential hazards associated with foods in order to decide which foods must be addressed in a HACCP plan.

Hazard Analysis Critical Control Point (HACCP): A food safety system designed to keep food safe throughout its flow in an establishment.

Risk: The chance that a given condition will lead to a hazard.

Risk: The chance that a condition or set of conditions will lead to a hazard.

Control Point (CP): Any step in the flow of food where a physical, chemical or biological hazard can be controlled but not eliminated.

Critical Control Point (CCP): A point, step or procedure at which a control can be applied and that is essential to prevent or eliminate a food safety hazard or reduce it to acceptable levels. Looked at in another way, a CCP is any point in production, preparation or handling where loss of control may result in an unacceptable health risk to the consumer.

Critical Limit: A standard or target that must be met for each preventive measure associated with a CCP. *Critical Limits* can be thought of as 'boundaries of safety' such as minimum temperature, time, chlorine levels in disinfectants, and physical dimensions.

The Seven Principles of HACCP

The HACCP system consists of seven principles. These principles outline how to develop a HACCP plan and should be applied as sequential tasks.

1. Conduct a *Hazard Analysis*.

2. Identify *Critical Control Points*.

3. Establish Critical Limits.

4. Monitor Critical Control Points.

5. Take corrective action.

6. Verify that the system is working.

7. Keep records.

PRINCIPLE ONE: Conduct a Hazard Analysis

This is one of the most important steps. An incorrect hazard analysis will lead to the development of an inadequate HACCP plan, so care should be taken. Contact your local public health inspector for help with your analysis or to locate a consultant in your area. A hazard analysis must be conducted for each existing and new product or item. In addition, the analysis must be reviewed when any changes are made in raw material, supplier, product formulation, preparation, production, storage, holding and serving. A hazard analysis includes:

• Reviewing the Flow of Food

The flow of food is the path food travels in your foodservice or food retail establishment from receiving to storing, preparing, cooking, holding, serving, cooling and reheating.

• Designing Flowcharts

A flowchart is a simple diagram showing the flow of food (*See Figure 8.0*). It is a way to picture what happens to a food product.

You will need to create flowcharts for all products/menu items. This task may not take as much time and effort as you may think; similar recipes call for similar flowcharts. For example, the recipes and flowcharts for chicken noodle soup and beef noodle soup will be very similar.

• Identifying Potentially Hazardous Foods

Review your food items and recipes (*See Figure 8.0 and 8.1*). Remember that a potentially hazardous food may be served alone or as an ingredient in a recipe. For

HACCP plans are designed to follow one direction only.

FIGURE 8.0 Chili Flowchart

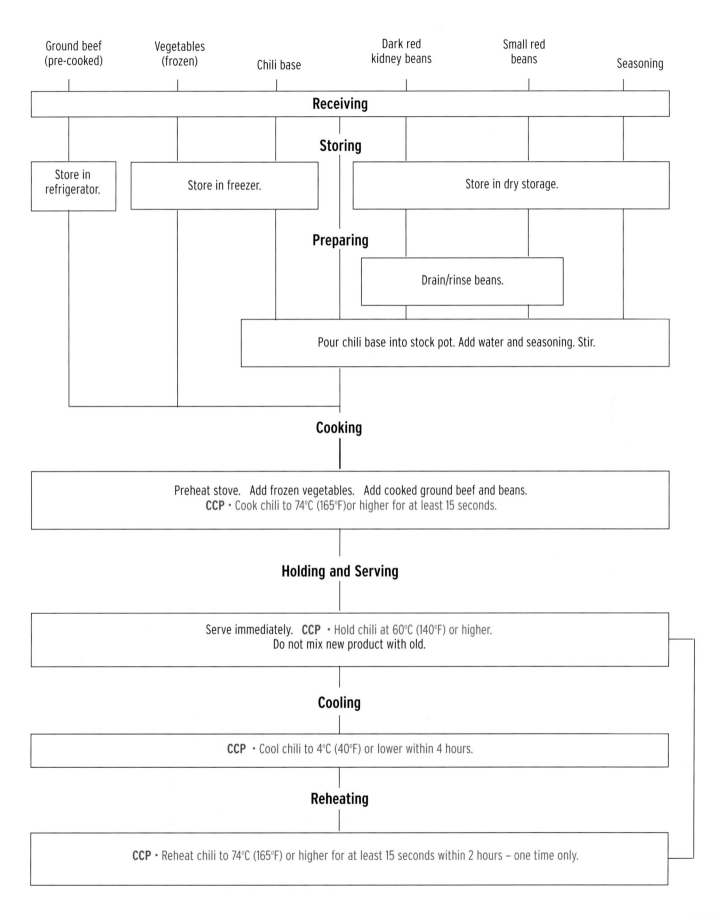

FIGURE 8.1 Chili Recipe with Critical Control Points

Ingredients	Weights and Measures
Ground beef (pre-cooked)	5 lb, 13 oz
Chili base	1 can
Small red beans	1 can
Dark red kidney beans	1 can
Vegetables (frozen)	2 packages
Seasoning	1 packet
Water	1 1/4 gal

PREPARING

1. Drain and rinse dark red and small red kidney beans. Set aside.
2. Pour chili base into stockpot. Add water and seasoning. Stir with wire whisk until all seasoning is dissolved.

COOKING

3. Preheat stove. Begin heating chili mix.
4. Break up any clumps in the frozen vegetables. Add to the chili mix. Stir with long-handled spoon.

CCP 5. Add cooked ground beef and beans and stir. **Continue heating chili until an internal temperature of 74°C (165°F) or higher is reached and held for at least 15 seconds.**

SERVING AND HOLDING

6. Serve immediately.

CCP 7. **Hold chili at 60°C (140°F) or higher.** Do not mix new product with old.

COOLING

CCP 8. Cool in shallow pans with a product depth not to exceed 2 inches. **Product temperature must reach 20°C (68°F) or lower within 2 hours, then reach 4° C (40° F) or lower within 4 hours.** Stir frequently.

9. Store at a product temperature of 4°C (40°F) or lower in a refrigerated unit. Cover.

REHEATING

CCP 10. **Reheat chili to a product temperature of 74°C (165°F) or higher for at least 15 seconds within 2 hours–one time only.**

SANITATION INSTRUCTIONS: Measure all temperatures with a cleaned and sanitized thermocouple or thermometer. Wash hands before handling food, after handling raw foods, and after any interruption that may contaminate hands. Wash, rinse and sanitize all equipment and utensils before and after use. Return all ingredients to refrigerated storage if preparation is interrupted.

* CCPs are highlighted in **boldface.**

example, chicken is often served as an ingredient in soup and as a main entrée.

Product properties, destinations and uses are variables to keep in mind when identifying hazards. It is also important to consider whether high risk members of the population (children, elderly, pregnant or those with weakened immune systems) may consume the product.

- **Identifying Hazards**

Now that you have determined the food items and recipes that use potentially hazardous foods, you need to decide what hazards can occur during the flow of food. Watch your employees in action and review your current records for any information on how food items are handled. While bacterial contamination and growth is a primary concern, you must also be aware of instances where there is risk of physical and chemical contamination.

PRINCIPLE TWO: Identify Critical Control Points

List the points in your operation where a control can be applied to prevent, eliminate or reduce a food safety hazard to acceptable levels. Note these on written recipes, flowcharts and systems schematics.

Remember, hazards can be reduced to safe levels or eliminated by CCPs. Examples of common CCPs include: cooking; cooling; formula control; and removing physical fragments. There may be more than one CCP at which a control can be applied to address the same hazard.

To help understand and identify CCPs, ask the following questions:

1. Is control at this step necessary for safety?

Yes - proceed to the next question
No - not a CCP

2. Is the step specifically designed to eliminate or reduce the likely occurrence of a hazard to an acceptable level?

Yes - CCP
No - proceed to next question

3. Could contamination with identified hazard(s) occur in excess of acceptable level(s) or could it increase to unacceptable levels?

Yes - proceed to next question
No - not a CCP

4. Will a subsequent step eliminate the identified hazard(s) or reduce likely occurrence to acceptable levels?

Yes - not a CCP
No - CCP

Example of a CCP:

During receiving, standard procedures are developed by management to evaluate products and check for visual signs of contamination. However, the raw chicken delivered at 4°C (40°F) may still be contaminated with invisible *Salmonella* bacteria. By answering all the above questions, it is determined that the risk of *Salmonella* can only be eliminated during the cooking process when the chicken is heated to 85°C (185°F) or higher for at least 15 seconds. This makes cooking the CCP in this example.

Remember that not all controls will become Critical Control Points. The degree of risk associated with a hazard should be assessed by considering its likelihood and severity of occurrence. This sometimes means separating safety concerns from quality concerns.

PRINCIPLE 3: Establish Critical Limits

Set the minimum standards that must be met at each CCP. Standards are times, temperatures or other requirements that must be met to keep a food item safe. Add these standards to your written directions and flowcharts. You may need more than one standard at each CCP. No matter how many you need, each Critical Limit should be:

- Measurable.

- Based on facts from experience, suppliers' advice, research data, or food regulations.

- Appropriate to the product when handled in a normal work environment, considering room temperature, number of employees and turnover.

- A clear direction to take a specific action, such as measuring a temperature or cooking an item for a certain length of time. For example, a Critical Limit for reheating chili is, "Heat rapidly on stove to an internal product temperature of 74°C (165°F) or higher for at least 15 seconds within 2 hours."

Beside limits for CCPs, write in standards to prevent contamination at other points in the flow of food. For example, "Wash, rinse and sanitize all equipment and utensils before and after use."

PRINCIPLE 4: Monitor CCPs

Monitoring involves scheduled measurement or observation to prevent the violation of Critical Limits. Monitoring detects loss of control at the CCP.

Successful monitoring depends on employees being involved in the process. They must know the CCPs and understand their Critical Limits.

All records and documents associated with monitoring must be signed by the person(s) responsible.

PRINCIPLE 5: Take Corrective Action

When you find a Critical Limit for a CCP is not being met, correct it right away. Many corrective actions are simple, such as continuing to heat an item if the end cooking temperature has not been reached. Other corrective actions may not be as simple, such as throwing out a food item. You may want an employee to ask a supervisor before taking action.

For example, the Critical Limit for holding baked chicken may read:

- "Hold baked chicken at 60°C (140°F) or higher until served."

The corrective action if the limit is not met may read:

- "If held over two hours, discard. If held less than two hours and temperature falls below 60°C (140°F), reheat to 74°C (165°F) or higher for at least 15 seconds — one time only."

PRINCIPLE 6: Verify that the System is Working

Establish procedures for verification. Confirm that your HACCP system is working properly through auditing, verification procedures, and tests such as random sampling. Verify that you have:

- Identified and assessed all hazards.

- Selected CCPs and set Critical Limits.

- Trained employees.

- Selected monitoring procedures and schedules.

NAME A MEASUREMENT FORM USED IN YOUR ESTABLISHMENT:

_____

- Calibrated monitoring equipment.

- Developed corrective actions.

PRINCIPLE 7: Set Up a Record-Keeping System

Accurate records are essential to a HACCP system. All HACCP procedures should be documented and records should be appropriate to the size and nature of the foodservice or food retail operation. Some ideas are to keep:

- Blank forms and a clipboard near work areas.

- Notebooks to write down what actions have been taken.

- All flowcharts and recipes near work areas, so employees can use them quickly.

- Blank temperature logs hung on equipment for easy use.

Remember, if records are easy to use, your employees are less likely to "*dry lab*", which means to record false data without actually measuring the temperature of the food.

The Written HACCP System

An illustration of what a HACCP system can look like in written form includes operational steps, hazards, CCPs, standards, types of monitoring, corrective actions, and records. Your local regulatory agency may also require a written HACCP plan that includes the food safety principles discussed in this chapter.

The written procedures you develop using Principles 1 to 7 provide you with a complete, flexible framework that allows your system to change as needed. The next step is to train your employees according to the HACCP system.

Adapting Your HACCP Plan

Your food safety training program may already cover much of the information employees will need to run a HACCP system. Key goals when adapting your program to support a HACCP system are to:

• Help your employees understand the basics of HACCP. When you first adopt the new system, your employees' greatest concern will be how it will affect the work they do. Reassure them that they are already using many of the right procedures. Explain their role in putting the system to work. Be sure to speak candidly with employees so they understand not only what they must do but feel free to ask questions.

• Discuss CCP monitoring procedures and record keeping.

• Help employees adjust their current skills to HACCP methods.

• Identify areas where employees lack knowledge or skills and design training to meet those needs.

Overall, training should be as practical as possible. Employees do not need to memorize the complete HACCP system and its terms. They need to understand the official food safety procedures that directly relate to their job.

HACCP Training

Assess each job for special training requirements in handling food, operating equipment and cleaning. Develop specific training objectives for employees based on what they need to do to keep food safe.

Task Analysis

Break down each task into specific duties and HACCP procedures. Add these to your task descriptions. An employee needs to learn from Day One that taking the final cooking temperature of a food is part of their job. Make it clear that not completing this task properly would be regarded as not meeting operating standards.

Learning Objectives

The learning objectives should state clearly the key skills an employee needs to fill the position. Examples include knowing how to correctly calibrate and use a thermometer, and fill out time/temperature logs.

Corrective Actions

Clearly explain the corrective actions that are expected of each employee should they discover that a Critical Limit is not being met. Ensure that they are able to complete the task independently, or that they know when to report to a supervisor for assistance.

Developing Your Training Program

Your overall approach to training should balance the importance of the topic with the need to make it interesting. Employees learn food safety most easily when they can put what they learn into action right away. They need to see or hear information, practice applying it, and receive timely feedback on their performance. The following are some general guidelines.

1. Tell them what they are going to be taught and why it is important to learn.

2. Present the material in various ways, including role-playing and videos.

3. Demonstrate steps and procedures.

4. Answer questions seriously and right away.

5. Let them practice or discuss what is presented.

6. Give feedback on their practical performance.

7. Review the material.

8. Test or evaluate the material.

9. Follow up training with monitoring.

10. Retrain if needed.

Choosing Training Methods

There are two basic methods for putting your program into action: individual training and group training.

Individual, or one-on-one training, assigns one or two trainees to an experienced employee for peer tutoring. The advantages of this method are several: training is job-focused, the trainees receive personal attention, there is the opportunity to apply the skill right away, and feedback is immediate. There are disadvantages, though. There is the possibility that the trainer is not a good teacher, that the trainees pick up the trainer's bad habits, and that the skill may not be learned.

Group training involves a group of trainees meeting with a trainer, usually in a session apart from their normal work. The advantages are that trainees can work with each other, discuss ideas and solve problems as a team. A uniform program can be developed for all trainees. Trainers can also use group exercises, such as games, role-playing, and team competitions to provide active learning. The disadvantages are that trainees get less personal attention and little chance to immediately practice new skills. This may result in a trainer who loses trainee attention during a long lecture.

Using the best elements from both of these training methods is recommended.

Another method, crash training — the attempt to cover a lot of material on the job in a very short time — is not recommended for topics as complex as HACCP and Food Safety.

Evaluating Your Training Program

In a HACCP system, on-the-job performance is the key measure of training success. After the training session, pay special attention to the results of your HACCP monitoring procedures. Ask yourself:

1. Did the training produce results on the job? Are employees meeting the training objectives related to CCPs and standards?

2. If the intended results were not produced, why not?

If you are not getting the results you intended, you may decide to work with the employees individually, ask for their opinion about why it is not working, schedule more training, or take another course of action.

Summary

• Hazard Analysis Critical Control Point (HACCP) is a food safety system designed to keep food safe throughout its flow in an establishment.

• A successful HACCP system is a combination of proper food handling procedures, monitoring techniques and record keeping to keep food safe.

• Generic HACCP plans should help your establishment develop its own plans.

• An effective HACCP plan is based on these 7 Principles:

1. Conduct a Hazard Analysis.

2. Identify Critical Control Points.

3. Establish Critical Limits.

4. Monitor Critical Control Points.

5. Take corrective action.

6. Verify that the system is working.

7. Keep records.

Consider This....

James, a food handler at a fancy hotel, Esquire in Calgary, had a date with one of the servers on Friday night after closing at 11:00pm. James was also scheduled to work the brunch buffet on Saturday morning at 9:00am. To save time (so he could sleep in an extra hour) James decided to make Esquire's signature buffet dessert, mini lemon meringue pies before he left. James checked the recipe for the pies and decided that it was fine to make the dish the night before. Knowing that the pies were loved because they were fresh he did not want to place the pies in the cooler and left them on a cart overnight.

The breakfast buffet was as successful as James' date; a good time was had by all. That was until late Sunday afternoon when the patrons who ate his pies started feeling ill.

What food safety rule was broken at Esquire?

How might Esquire adjust their procedures to make sure that this error is not repeated?

Answers can be found on page 203.

EXERCISE 8

1. **When you first set up a HACCP system, introduce it to employees by:**
   a. Telling them that those who don't adapt to the system will be moved to non-food prep duties.
   b. Assigning them to memorize all HACCP terms.
   c. Keeping the lines of communication open so employees understand what they must do and feel free to ask questions.
   d. Putting a notice on the bulletin board.

2. **Food safety training objectives for food handlers should be centred on:**
   a. CCPs and standards.
   b. Decreasing food waste.
   c. More expensive entrées.
   d. Controlling portion size.

3. **The practice of entering a temperature in a log without really measuring the temperature is called:**
   a. Monitoring.
   b. Verifying.
   c. Standard setting.
   d. Dry lab.

4. **HACCP food safety systems focus on:**
   a. Protecting food at all times during the flow of food.
   b. Verifying that produce is fresh when delivered.
   c. Protecting meat from mould.
   d. Producing food only in large quantities.

5. **Flowcharts are:**
   a. Recipes with more than seven ingredients.
   b. Time and temperature logs.
   c. Diagrams that show the flow of food.
   d. Charts showing the growth of bacteria.

6. **Which one of the following should you do if you find a recipe is too difficult to handle as it is written?**
   a. Make sure you are the one to prepare it.
   b. Simplify the steps or ingredients in it.
   c. Offer the menu item for one week only.
   d. Lower the price on the menu.

7. **Which one of the following is a *corrective* action for handling chili?**
   a. Hold chili at 60°C (140°F) or higher until served.
   b. Cool chili from 60°C to 4°C (140°F to 40°F) or lower within four hours.
   c. Reheat chili to an internal temperature of 74°C (165°F) or higher if holding temperature falls below 60°C (140°F).
   d. Place chili in shallow pans with a product depth of 5cm (2 inches) or less into an ice bath.

8. **Temperature logs should be kept:**
   a. In your office.
   b. Near employee work areas.
   c. In various locations.
   d. Near employee break areas.

Answers can be found on page 198.

TEST YOUR FOOD SAFETY

1. True or False: An outbreak of foodborne illness is always contained locally. (*See Terms to Know, page 116*)

2. True or False: Facility prerequisites only apply to the kitchen of a foodservice establishment. (*See Prerequisite Programs, page 116*)

3. True or False: Prerequisite programs should be designed and assessed during the implementation of HACCP. (*See Prerequisite Programs, page 115*)

4. True or False: Crisis management needs to be well planned but does not need to be documented. (*See In Case of Emergency - Crisis Management, page 118*)

5. True or False: If an incident occurs, avoid getting the local Public Health Unit involved. (*See In Case of Emergency - Crisis Management, page 118*)

Introduction

An effective HACCP system is built on a solid foundation of prerequisite programs. These programs act to control the basic environmental, operating and personnel related conditions necessary for the production of safe food. Many of the conditions and practices are specified in federal, provincial and local regulations and guidelines.

A complete food safety system is designed to help you ensure that the food you provide to your customers is safe. Despite your best efforts, a foodborne illness outbreak can still occur. In case of emergency, a written plan will guide your response and help to identify the resources and procedures necessary for a quick resolution to the crisis.

Prerequisite Programs

All prerequisite programs should be designed and assessed during the implementation of a HACCP plan. They are then documented and audited regularly for effectiveness.

The following are examples of common prerequisite programs.

FACILITY DESIGN

Facilities should be planned according to sanitary design principles. Pay attention to efficient product flow and traffic through the facility. Opportunities for cross-contamination from raw to ready-to-eat food should be minimized as much as possible. Check with national, provincial and local sanitation and building code standards for guidelines.

LEARNING OBJECTIVES

After completing this chapter, you should be able to:

- Recognize the importance of Prerequisite Programs to your HACCP system.
- Identify and implement Prerequisite Programs suited to your unique foodservice operation.

- Understand the need for a Crisis Management strategy and take steps to implement one in your organization.

Facility prerequisites also apply to the design of staff washrooms and eating areas, drainage and sewage systems, waste containers, lighting and building exteriors (*See Chapter 11*).

SUPPLIER AND PRODUCT CONTROL

Select suppliers with reputable food safety programs in place. You may want to request written assurance that they follow a HACCP program (*See Chapter 8*).

SPECIFICATIONS

There should be written specifications for all ingredients, recipes, products, and packaging materials. All recipes need to be standardized so that staff can provide accurate information in case of allergies or foodborne illness (*See Chapter 2 and 8*).

EQUIPMENT

All equipment must be properly installed and used. Develop a documented equipment maintenance and calibration program that outlines:

- The preventive maintenance activities that need to be performed.

- The materials and chemicals required to operate equipment.

- A description and schedule for calibration activities for equipment such as thermometers and scales.

- Specific staff members responsible for each task.

CLEANING AND SANITATION

All procedures for cleaning and sanitation of equipment, food contact surfaces, utensils and the facilities should be written out and enforced. Build a master sanitation schedule for staff to follow (*See Chapter 12*).

PERSONAL HYGIENE

Make sure that every person entering food handling areas follows strict personal hygiene protocols. These requirements are meant to prevent or minimize contamination of food and food contact surfaces by biological, chemical or physical hazards (*See Chapter 3*).

EDUCATION AND TRAINING

All employees should receive training in: safe food handling; personal hygiene; cleaning and sanitation procedures; equipment use and maintenance; workplace safety; and, their role in the established HACCP program. Keep copies of all related documents such as certificates or report cards.

To understand HACCP procedures, staff need to have a basic understanding of food safety. This information includes:

• Benefits of practicing food safety.

• Which foods are potentially hazardous.

• How contamination can occur at any point in the flow of food.

• Time and temperature standards for potentially hazardous foods and the Temperature Danger Zone.

• Links between good personal hygiene and food safety.

• Employees' role in preventing cross-contamination and in preventing foodborne illness.

Food safety training may be an important requirement for hiring, promotions, raises and bonuses, and should be directly incorporated in performance appraisals.

CHEMICAL CONTROL

Non-food chemicals have to be dispensed and handled according to manufacturer's instructions. Chemicals can leave residue on equipment and surfaces leading to contamination of foods. Remember that chemicals should only be stored in original or clearly labelled bottles – *never* in food containers.

Only use chemicals approved for use in foodservice or food retail operations and keep material safety data sheets (MSDS) on file. Establish easy-to-follow procedures for proper use of chemicals (*See Chapter 12*).

RECEIVING AND STORAGE

Receiving and storage records are a necessary control measure to protect food from contamination, damage and spoilage. All foods, products and raw materials should be received and stored under sanitary conditions. Make sure that staff assigned to these tasks understand receiving specifications, and that they check temperatures of refrigerated and frozen products prior to accepting shipments. Storage areas should be monitored and maintained at suitable temperatures/humidity levels (*See Chapters 5 & 6*).

MY SANITATION SCHEDULE IS LOCATED:

_____

PEST CONTROL

Establish effective pest control plans and keep all support documentation (*See Chapter 13*). Ensure that there is an effective written pest control program for the premises and equipment that includes:

- The identification of the person assigned responsibility for pest control.

- Where applicable, the name of the pest control company contracted.

- A list of chemicals used, the concentration, the location where applied, method and frequency of application.

- Map of trap locations.

- The type and frequency of inspection to verify the effectiveness of the program.

RECALL AND TRACEABILITY

Supervisors and managers must have detailed procedures to follow in case a food safety hazard is discovered. The plan must facilitate the rapid *recall* of any food product implicated. The need for public warnings may also be considered.

Customize Your Program

The important thing to remember when developing prerequisite programs is that prerequisites have to be customized to suit the needs for your business. No two foodservice or food retail operations will have identical plans!

For example, the equipment prerequisite for a retail store would detail preventive maintenance procedures to avoid unexpected failure of equipment like fridges or meat slicers. In a restaurant, the equipment prerequisite would include routine maintenance and calibration of an oven as a control to ensure that food is cooked to the minimum internal temperature for food safety.

Prerequisite programs can easily be incorporated into start-up and shut-down procedures. They form the framework for your HACCP program, reduce multiple CCPs and therefore reduce risk!

In Case of Emergency – Crisis Management

With growing food distribution networks and the globalization of trade, food is increasingly being moved across domestic and international borders. As a result, foodborne illness outbreaks can result in cases that cross all boundaries from local to international.

In Canada, the responsibility for responding to emergency situations involving food items is shared by foodservice operators, local and regional health authorities, provincial and territorial governments, and federal authorities (*See Appendix A for additional information*).

Throughout the ADVANCED.*fst*® program, you have learned the food safety principles needed to make sure that you offer safe food to your customers. Unfortunately, no matter how prepared you are, a foodborne *incident* or *outbreak* may still occur in your establishment. Such a situation may take the form of a customer complaint, contamination of food by microbial, chemical or physical substances, natural disaster, or deliberate tampering.

It is important that every foodservice or food retail provider have a written plan for dealing with situations in case they occur. Swift action by managers/employees can prevent an incident from becoming a crisis.

Be Prepared

Develop a strategy that allows you to meet the needs of your operation while fostering public trust and confidence in the safety of the food supply. Whether you write a comprehensive report or a step-by-step list depends on the size of your operation.

There are a number of steps you can take to prepare for a real or perceived risk.

- **Designate a Crisis Management Team** to develop your *outbreak response* strategy. Within the team, assign specific staff members, according to experience and expertise, to create protocols outlining how your operation will respond.

  Members of your team can include owners, general managers, managers, chefs, finance and public relations managers. It is important to choose **one person** to lead all communication activities with the media, public and other stakeholders.

- **Brainstorm to identify the nature of the risk** – preparedness is vital to successful *risk management*. Remember that risks include biological, physical, allergen and chemical contamination, as well as disasters such as flood and power-outages. The type of customer and size of operation should be considered when assessing potential hazards.

- **Write out simple instructions** and put them in an easy-to-find place. In foodborne illness outbreaks, steps include removing the suspect food from production or shelves, obtaining a sample of the food for testing, contacting public health officials, and excluding employees who may be a source of contamination from handling food.

- **Post an emergency contact list by the telephone.** This list should include your local public health unit, police and fire departments, and poison control.

GATHER INFORMATION ...

- When did you become ill? What were the symptoms and when did you first experience them?

- What did you eat and drink at our establishment and when? Who else consumed them? Did they become ill?

- Did you seek medical attention?

In the event of an incident that may be related to tampering activity, notify local/regional law enforcement agencies immediately. In cases where terrorist activity is suspected the *RCMP National Operations Centre* should also be contacted, regardless of police jurisdiction.

- **Set up response protocols.** Perception and opinion often determine the resolution of high concern, high stress or emotionally charged issues. Central to effective communication is an organization's ability to establish, maintain, and increase trust and credibility.

  Respond to all customer concerns and evaluate complaints. Always be courteous, empathetic, and honest without assuming responsibility on the establishment's part. Approach the issue with competence and a dedication to swift resolution. Ask, and record the responses to questions that will help you understand what happened.

  Determine whether public health authorities have been contacted. You may want to suggest to the customer that they contact public health or contact them yourself.

- **Train staff.** All staff should be trained to follow the policies and procedures outlined in your plan.

Outbreak Response

In the event of an investigation by the local health unit, every effort should be made to co-operate. Inspection authorities may ask for information related to the incident. You should be able to quickly gather all HACCP and prerequisite program records/documents to determine whether there has been a breakdown in controls. Also supply employee illness reports and, if possible, information on distribution of food.

If an outbreak occurs, only the designated spokesperson such as the general manager, the manager on duty, or other qualified person should communicate with media as needed. The media play a critical role in risk communication because they deliver much of the information that the public receives. Provide meaningful, relevant and accurate information in a clear and understandable way.

It may be necessary to seek expert advice relating to public relations, laboratory testing and crisis management.

Resolution

Once the incident is resolved, take the time to assess your establishment's response. Determine what the strengths and weaknesses were in areas such as communication, effectiveness of HACCP systems, response time and staff preparedness. Learn from this incident and integrate the lessons into your prerequisite and HACCP programs to further safeguard your business and customers. Take steps to prevent a crisis from recurring by practicing good food safety habits.

Summary

- Prerequisite programs are the foundation of an effective HACCP system.

- Programs and their components will vary from operation to operation, reflecting the needs of each business.

- Programs should be evaluated and updated regularly.

- Being prepared for an incident or outbreak can help you control the situation and its impact on your business.

- Employing good food safety practices is key to risk management in food handling environments.

WORD SEARCH

Find ten words related to the Foundation Programs discussed in this chapter.

Find the hidden words within the grid of letters.

```
L C E E E W E R U D Q Y Y H S F F X Z T
P A H F Z W H I B A X W G P H A K N S U
E A I E B I I S S Y J B E S O C X P W X
K O Z A M Z M K J F S C T F D I U N L Q
Z Y J O I I R O X A I C A J F L H X L B
Y R G J Y Z C N T F C I R K Y I G W C B
G C C L M P C A I S Z F T N H T S M J T
O S Z P L Z S C L D U V S A D Y H G I S
I F K S U K A I S C T C Z Q X D D H K W
R R N T O T U I J V O S K V V E W P F V
U O Q Z I E A N P M W N D P I S C G B Q
E H L O R E C A L L O Q T L M I Z W K G
X E N Y T I L I B A E C A R T G G W N Z
O S J V O B T O D F N I N E O N S I D J
R E S P O N S E P R O T O C O L N E I Q
H E B B N M K D X L J K H G I I M I K G
Q A H T A H L W A K Z Y C P A U Q O S B
H U C V K H T F Y A V O E R M C V H V R
V O M C G J I G D Q W U T I U Q G X P X
L P V K P R W H K R X O B T X T R J C S
```

CHEMICAL CONTROL	RECALL	STRATEGY
CUSTOMIZE	RESPONSE PROTOCOL	TRACEABILITY
FACILITY DESIGN	RISK	TRAINING
HACCP	SPECIFICATIONS	

EXERCISE 9

1. **If an outbreak occurs you should:**
   a. Encourage all staff to talk to the media if approached.
   b. Shred any documents that might link your operation to the outbreak.
   c. Appoint one spokesperson to communicate with the media if required.
   d. Invite local Public Health officials to try the product involved.

2. **To understand HACCP procedures, employees need to understand:**
   a. Which foods are potentially hazardous.
   b. The importance of good personal hygiene.
   c. Their role in preventing cross-contamination.
   d. All of the above.

3. **HACCP prerequisite programs:**
   a. Do not affect the production of safe food.
   b. Do not control environmental conditions related to safe food production.
   c. Are the foundation of an effective HACCP system.
   d. Are identical in every workplace.

4. **Which of the following is not a common prerequisite program?**
   a. Supplier and product control.
   b. Cost of goods sold.
   c. Equipment.
   d. Pest Control.

5. **After an incident has been resolved:**
   a. Assure staff that nothing like this could ever happen again.
   b. Review your response and discuss/document how it could have been improved.
   c. Integrate lessons learned into your existing HACCP systems.
   d. Both b and c.

6. **Crisis Management:**
   a. Cannot be planned.
   b. Applies only to media relations.
   c. Could be required for a customer complaint or a natural disaster.
   d. Is only important for food retail operations, not small restaurants.

7. **Personal Hygiene:**
   a. Is not a prerequisite program.
   b. Cannot be controlled in a HACCP system.
   c. Is a program that must apply to every person entering a food handling area.
   d. Is only required as a program if staff have not completed a food safety training course.

8. **Crisis Management Teams should:**
   a. Develop a crisis response strategy.
   b. Be comprised mainly of regular customers.
   c. Can share all crisis related tasks including dealing with the media.
   d. Both a and c.

Answers can be found on page 199.

TEST YOUR FOOD SAFETY

1. True or False: Very young, elderly and ill diners may be especially vulnerable to foodborne illnesses. (*See Institutional Service Operations, page 124*)

2. True or False: Provide customers with short-handled serving spoons at a food bar. (*See Food Bars and Other Self-Service Arrangements, page 125*)

3. True or False: It is acceptable to reuse cardboard boxes as delivery containers for food. (*See Off-Site Delivery, page 126*)

4. True or False: Mobile units serving potentially hazardous foods must meet the same food safety standards as permanent operations. (*See Mobile Vending Units, page 129*)

5. True or False: Vending machines can be installed anywhere in a foodservice operation. (*See Vending Machines, page 130*)

Operating Models

Recognizing that no two operations are exactly alike, in this chapter we discuss guidelines that may be more specific to your type of business. Look at your operation, step-by-step, and determine which model of operation style describes your food delivery system. In this way, individual establishments may customize pertinent details or add components from more than one model to accurately reflect their operation. For example, your operation may include aspects similar to those in *Central Kitchens* and in *Temporary Foodservices*.

Retail Grocery Operations

Retail grocery is one of the primary sources of food purchased by Canadian consumers. Depending on the size of the operation, your store may sell whole produce, prepackaged foods requiring refrigeration or freezer control, meats either prepackaged or butchered on-site, deli products, baked goods, bulk foods, and/or prepared food for consumption off-site. This diverse product base within a single operation results in an increased opportunity for food safety violations. Retail operators must therefore be committed to providing a sanitary environment for consumers.

In food retail, the HACCP analysis is process-related rather than product-related. When you survey your store, process flow and Standard Operating Procedures (SOP), incorporate guidelines for facility design and HACCP-based principles from all areas in this chapter that apply. In addition, take the following key controls into consideration.

• Ensure proper temperature control and monitoring.

LEARNING OBJECTIVES

After completing this chapter, you should be able to:

● Understand the basic food safety needs of retail grocery, fast food service, full service and institutional service operations.
● Adapt HACCP principles to the type of service your operation provides.

Central Kitchen: A kitchen used to prepare food for large groups.

Food Bar: A display of hot and/or cold foods where customers either serve themselves or are helped by attendants.

Mobile Vending Units: A cart, stand or kiosk that is operated either from a fixed location or on an established daily route, from which food is served or provided to the public with or without charge.

Temporary Units: A unit that is licensed to operate in a specific location for a certain period of time.

Vending Machines: Money-, card-, or key-operated self-service devices that dispense servings of food in bulk or in packages.

- Ensure practices are in place to prevent cross-contamination during receiving, storage, preparation and retail display. This includes microbiological, chemical and physical matter contaminants and priority allergens.

- Ensure sanitation procedures are adhered to, conducted at appropriate frequencies and that their execution is documented.

- Ensure pest control measures are implemented and documented.

Fast Food Service Operations

Fast food service operations usually feature short waiting times for service, limited menus, and service counters where customers wait, pick up and pay for their food. Such operations range from small stands to large sites with drive-through and sit-down dining facilities. Full service and institutional service operations may offer carry-out, which is similar to fast food service operations. Standardize procedures:

- Focus training on food handling, cooking times and temperatures, and personal hygiene.

- Cook all potentially hazardous foods to safe internal temperatures.

- Prepare only small batches of food in advance.

Institutional Service Operations

Institutional service operations include nursing homes and hospitals, child care facilities, schools at all levels, corporate dining rooms, and cafeterias. These operations usually serve groups of customers and may need to provide special diets and off-hour meals. Manager/operators often plan menus and order supplies well in advance.

Nursing homes, hospitals and schools must be aware that they serve customers — the young, elderly and ill — who may be especially vulnerable to foodborne illnesses.

Food Choices

Use only:

• Federally and provincially/territorially inspected, commercially processed foods. Never use homemade and home-canned foods.

• Pasteurized milk and milk products.

• Pasteurized eggs — to guard against *Salmonella*. If you use shell eggs, cook them until they are firm to 63°C (145°F) for 15 seconds. Customers requesting a runny yolk egg must recognize that pathogens are not destroyed until the yolk has completely coagulated.

On-Site Delivery

To keep foods safe while in transit:

• Sanitize trays, utensils and delivery equipment. Store them in clean areas or sanitized containers.

• Separate foods when packaging them to prevent temperature changes and cross-contamination. Separately package condiments and utensils.

• Use containers designed to maintain temperatures when transporting food.

• Deliver food without unnecessary delay to adhere to the time and temperature requirement.

Once food is onsite:
• Reheat hot foods to 74°C (165°F) for at least 15 seconds, then hold at 60°C (140°F) or higher. Deliver cold foods at 4°C (40°F) or lower, and hold at this temperature until service.

Food Bars and Other Self-Service Areas

Food bars, buffets and cafeterias usually include a display of hot or cold foods. Customers walk by, either help themselves or are served by attendants, and then bring their food back to their tables. Customers often return for more servings. Food is often displayed for extended time periods in high-traffic areas.

Special precautions are needed to control temperatures and physical contamination.

• Label all items so that customers do not need to sample or return them.

• Reheat hot foods to 74°C (165°F) for at least 15 seconds, then hold at 60°C (140°F) or higher. Hold cold items at 4°C (40°F) or lower (*see Figure 10.0*).

• Put ready-to-eat displayed foods on plates — not directly on ice. Ice surrounding chilled items must drain away from food containers. Sanitize drip pans after each use.

• Check food temperatures with a thermometer every two hours. Record temperatures in a log.

• In areas displaying chilled items, use lighting that will not raise food temperatures. Place plastic shields around lights to guard against broken glass or use plastic-coated lights.

• Provide tongs or a long-handled ladle for each item so customers do not touch the food.

• Place plastic sneeze guards or shields at a minimum of 35 cm (14 inches) but no higher than 1.2 m (48 inches) above the food in a direct line between the customer's face and the food. Please check with the local regulatory authority for specifications.

• Do not re-use ice, vegetable, or plant decorations.

FIGURE 10.0 Holding Units

Servers should:

- Give customers clean tableware each time they go through the food line.

- Alert customers about supervising their children.

- Remove any food containers, serving dishes and utensils that customers have touched, tasted, or contaminated in any way.

Central Kitchens

Central kitchens are often used to prepare food for large groups. They may serve food on-site or provide for services such as offsite delivery, catering, mobile and *temporary units* and *vending machines*. These extension operations are discussed later in this chapter.

Central kitchens must follow all safe food handling principles. They must use the proper procedures and equipment for chilling and holding, in addition they must provide:

- Equipment for deep-chilling large quantities of food at -3°C to 0°C (27°F to 32°F).

- Refrigerators for short-term storage at a food product internal temperature of 4°C (40°F) or lower.

- Freezers for storing already chilled or frozen foods at -18°C (0°F) or lower.

Operations that cook meat, such as rare roast beef, to lower than 63°C (145°F) for 3 minutes or 54°C (130°F) for 121 minutes must use special equipment and specifications.

Off-Site Delivery

Since foods are often cooked but not immediately consumed, many possibilities exist for contamination and time-temperature abuse during delivery.

Control production, holding, packaging and delivery:

- Cook hot foods to a proper internal product temperature, then hold at 60°C (140°F) or higher.

- Deliver cold items at 4°C (40°F) or lower.

- Label foods with proper storage, shelf life and reheating instructions for employees at off-site locations and customers.

- All vehicles and equipment must be clean, sanitized and free from possible contaminants.

- Package food to prevent temperature changes and cross-contamination. Separately package condiments and plastic utensils.

- Covered food containers must sustain food temperatures, allow air to circulate, keep food from spilling or leaking, and be disposable or easy to clean and stackable. Only use containers designed to transport food — do not reuse cardboard boxes as food containers (*see Figure 10.1*).

- Consider packing an extra meal and measuring its temperature at the end of the delivery route to determine how well your equipment protects the food.

- Load foods quickly.

- Plan routes so food is delivered within a safe time and at a safe temperature.

- Food transport equipment that might come in contact with food items must be constructed with non-toxic materials which are easy to maintain and clean (such as stainless steel or food-grade plastic).

- Inspect delivery vehicles to ensure that they are free from possible contaminants. Keep them clean and well maintained (breakdowns may spoil food).

- Service areas for delivery vehicles, such as garages, should be clean, dry, and away from food storage and preparation areas.

Catering

Caterers provide food for airlines, private parties, events, and public and corporate affairs. Caterers may bring in ready-to-eat food or they may prepare food in mobile or temporary units, in rented facilities, or with the customer's own equipment. Review all guidelines discussed in *Central Kitchens, Off-Site Delivery* and *Temporary Foodservice*. In addition:

- Reheat hot foods **only once** to 74°C (165°F) for at least 15 seconds within two hours, before holding and serving at 60°C (140°F) or higher.

- Check all food temperatures with a clean and sanitized thermometer every two hours. Record temperatures in a log book.

- Be sure there is a safe, drinkable water supply (including enough hot water) for cooking and washing and adequate toilet and hand-washing facilities.

- Be sure there is enough power to run your cooking and cooling equipment.

- Be sure there are adequate facilities for garbage disposal.

- Check for signs of insects and rodents. Take any precautions neccesary to ensure that all food and food contact surfaces are protected from contamination by pests.

For outdoor catering, such as barbecues and cookouts:

- Deliver raw meat frozen, wrapped, and on ice. Consider supplying ice chests if customers wish to transport food themselves. Chill these containers before filling them with potentially hazardous foods.

- Deliver all milk products in a refrigerated vehicle or on ice.

- Take special care when handling potentially hazardous foods, such as meat or fish. Store them separately from ready-to-eat foods.

FIGURE 10.1 Delivery of Food Off-Site

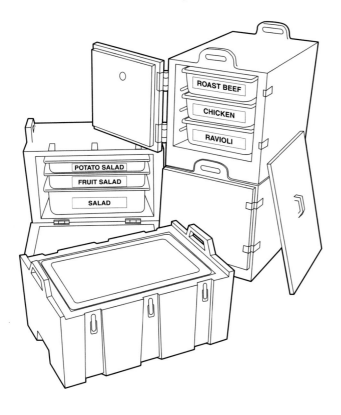

ROAST BEEF
CHICKEN
RAVIOLI

POTATO SALAD
FRUIT SALAD
SALAD

- Never allow homemade or home-canned foods to be served.

- Supervise customers' behaviour around cooking equipment and food displays.

- If food is left with the customer after the catered engagement, provide proper storage, shelf life and reheating instructions.

Outdoor Service

Outdoor service includes table service, food bars and other self-service operations. Check with your local health unit for specific regulations on outdoor service, overhead protection and enclosure details. Supervise food choice, production, temperatures, packaging and service:

- Provide a portable handwash station with a safe, potable water supply including hot and cold running water, soap in a dispenser, and single use hand towels. The station must meet local requirements.

- A two compartment stainless steel sink should be supplied, large enough to facilitate washing and sanitizing of equipment and utensils.

- Hold cold foods at 4°C (40°F) or lower. Check food temperatures with a thermometer every two hours, more often in hot weather. Record temperatures in a log.

- Hold hot foods at 60°C (140°F) or higher. Check food temperatures with a thermometer every two hours. Record temperatures in a log.

- Food removed from temperature control must be discarded after two hours.

- For outdoor buffets, prepare smaller batches of each item and whether or not used up, regularly discard and replace those batches. Do not mix new food into old.

- Put ready-to-eat displayed foods on plates — not directly

on ice. Ice surrounding chilled items must drain away from food containers. Sanitize drip pans after each use.

- In hot weather, check ice-making equipment and arrange for enough staff to provide fast service.

- Use chilled plates to serve cold items.

- Serve condiments, such as ketchup, in sealed containers.

- Provide windscreens to keep dirt and pests out of food.

- Set up foodservice and dining areas away from portable toilets and privies.

Temporary Food Premises, and Mobile Vendors

Mobile Vending Units

Mobile units include hotdog stands, catering trucks, driveable and portable serving and preparation facilities. They may range from soft-drink stands to elaborate field kitchens. If the unit serves only beverages and ready-to-eat packaged foods, health requirements may be relatively simple. Check with your local health unit for additional requirements.

If the unit prepares and serves potentially hazardous foods, all food safety and HACCP practices applicable for permanent foodservice operations must be followed. Additional provisions include:

- Vending carts should be constructed from easy to clean, durable materials.

- Enough hot and cold water is required to adequately allow for proper handwashing and the cleaning and sanitizing of utensils.

- The unit should be returned to an approved base of operations when not in use. It is important that food supplies are stored in safe, sanitary conditions.

- The unit must be cleaned and sanitized after every use.

- A potable water tank is required and should have a minimum capacity of 36 litres with a waste water holding tank incorporated into the design of the unit.

- The operator of catering trucks or mobile vending units must refrain from smoking while serving food.

Temporary Foodservices

The Food Retail and Food Services Code defines a temporary unit as a unit that is licensed to operate in a specific location for a certain period of time. While normally issued for less than 14 days per year, licenses may extend for an entire season. Locations may include special events, farmers' markets, concessions at fairs and festivals. As with mobile units, local health departments usually specify the requirements that must be met.

In most cases, temporary foodservices should not cook potentially hazardous foods. Exceptions include pre-prepared or pre-packaged foods and foods that require limited preparation, such as hot dogs. If local laws allow the preparation of potentially hazardous foods, review the requirements for *Catering* and *Off-Site Delivery*. In addition:

- Facilities must have a floor and roof built to keep out environmental contaminants such as dust, rain, birds, etc.

MY OPERATING MODEL IS:

_____

- Food must be prepared in a commercial kitchen under sanitary conditions.

- Pre-package food for individual service.

- All mechanical refrigerator, freezer and hot holding units must be sufficient in number and capacity to keep potentially hazardous foods out of the Temperature Danger Zone.

- Thawed, ready-to-eat, potentially hazardous foods should not be delivered or stored in direct contact with water or ice.

- Have potable water available for handwashing. Hot water should be kept at a minimum temperature of 43°C (110°F).

- Have potable water available for cleaning and sanitizing and hand washing. If utensils cannot be sanitized, single-service articles must be used. Hot water must be at a minimum temperature of 45°C (113°F) for manual dishwashing).

- A two compartment stainless steel sink must be supplied. The sinks must be large enough to immerse equipment and utensils, and be supplied with hot and cold running water.

- Potable water and waste tanks must meet the requirements outlined by public health authorities.

Vending Machines

Vending machines are money-, card-, or key-operated self-service devices that store and dispense food or beverages. These machines can carry a variety of hot and cold foods, including potentially hazardous foods. These foods are often ready-to-eat and packaged by a supplier. If you have vending machines, you are responsible for protecting the foods that are dispensed. Choose the proper facilities and equipment protection:

1. Choose reputable vending suppliers (*See General Purchasing Guidelines, Chapter 5*).

2. Check that vending supplies are properly packaged by your supplier:

- Fruits and vegetables that have an edible peel or outer surface, such as apples or celery, must be washed, dried and wrapped in food-grade packaging before being placed in the vending machine.

- Foods must be stored in sealed, moisture-resistant packages. Packaged potentially hazardous foods (such as wrapped sandwiches to be microwaved) must be dispensed in their original containers or wrappers.

3. Select machines that:

- Keep food out of the Temperature Danger Zone. Each machine with hot or cold storage capacity must have an automatic system that shuts down the vending mechanism if the temperature is out of the safety zone.

- Have tubes, chutes and delivery orifices that are protected from hand or lip contact.

- Divert splashes or drips away from the container receiving food by means of barriers or drip aprons.

- Have food-contact surfaces that are easily cleanable, corrosion-resistant, and non-absorbent.

- Have a self-closing door to protect against accidental or malicious contamination.

- Are Canadian Automatic Merchandising Association (CAMA) listed (or the equivalent).

4. Train employees to use good personal hygiene when servicing and refilling machines. Employees should wash their hands before and after these tasks.

5. Install machines away from garbage containers, sewer drains and pipes and in areas that are pest-free and where ceilings, walls and floors can be kept clean.

6. Be sure there is a safe supply of drinkable water for beverage machines. Guard against cross-connections due to faulty or corroded pipes (*See Chapter 11*).

Summary

- Critical care should be taken when serving food to the elderly, children, the sick, and pregnant women.

- Make sure the establishment has good and adequate holding and transporting equipment that can maintain the temperature of the foods.

- Make sure the equipment is in good repair and adequately protects food.

- Keep hot foods hot — above 60°C (140°F), and cold foods cold — below 4°C (40°F).

- Check with the local regulatory authority for specific operation requirements.

- Properly functioning vending machines keep food out of the Temperature Danger Zone.

Consider This....

Terry, owner of a popular neighbourhood pub in Mississauga wanted to give back to his community by organizing a charity marathon. In addition to meeting with organizers, helping with registration and contacting sponsors, Terry donated boxed lunches to the race volunteers. The meal consisted of bento-style lunch boxes containing luncheon meat, teriyaki beef, fried chicken, and rice. Approximately 300 lunches were distributed to volunteers stationed along the running route.

The lunch boxes were prepared at Terry's restaurant beginning at 6:00 am on the morning of the marathon. Needing some extra kitchen help Terry had enlisted his 12-year-old daughter, who was not trained in proper food handling practices, to pack the boxes. Terry's wife delivered the lunches to the volunteers using her own car.

Ninety-four of the volunteers reported becoming ill with vomiting and diarrhea within 1.5-5 hours of eating the lunches; the illness lasted up to four days for some volunteers. The culprit was a toxin caused by *Staphylococcus aureus*. The bacteria were recovered from eight stool samples as well as from samples of meat in left over lunch boxes.

What went wrong that contributed to the outbreak?

Answers can be found on page 203.

EXERCISE 10

1. **When holding hot food, fast-food operations should:**
   a. Limit holding time and regularly check temperatures.
   b. Hold large batches at temperatures as low as possible.
   c. Hold hot foods at 21°C (70°F).
   d. Use holding equipment to reheat food.

2. **If an institution serves eggs to very young, elderly, or ill diners, it should:**
   a. Store the eggs at room temperature.
   b. Use pasteurized eggs to guard against *Salmonella*.
   c. Only use shell eggs.
   d. Offer lightly cooked shell eggs in omelettes and scrambled eggs.

3. **When serving food outdoors:**
   a. Mix cold food into warm food.
   b. Serve ketchup and mayonnaise in large, uncovered bowls.
   c. Put ready-to-eat food directly on ice.
   d. Serve cold items on chilled plates.

4. **Food to be delivered hot should be transferred to delivery containers:**
   a. In the early morning for afternoon deliveries.
   b. At proper internal product temperatures.
   c. At 4°C (40°F).
   d. In reused cardboard containers.

5. **During a catering job, if your customer asks you to serve home-canned tomatoes:**
   a. Accept the tomatoes and heat them to 60°C (140°F).
   b. Accept the tomatoes and cool them to 4°C (40°F).
   c. Reject the tomatoes unless they are preserved in glass containers.
   d. Reject the tomatoes because home-canned foods must never be used.

6. **During a catering job, if you find signs of rodents in the kitchen area:**
   a. Refuse to prepare or serve food in that area.
   b. Have your employees wear gloves.
   c. Immediately set traps to catch them.
   d. Cover all holding pans.

7. **In a temporary kitchen, if knives, forks and spoons can not be sanitized:**
   a. Wipe them on a clean towel before use.
   b. Rinse them in warm water.
   c. Use single-service utensils.
   d. Spray mild disinfectant on them, then wipe them off.

8. **In a vending machine, packaged potentially hazardous foods (such as wrapped sandwiches to be microwaved) must be:**
   a. Stored at 21°C (70°F).
   b. Removed from their wrapper before being put in the machine.
   c. Dispensed in their original containers or wrappers.
   d. Wrapped in metal foil.

Answers can be found on page 199.

NOTES

FACILITIES MAINTENANCE

PART 4.0

CHAPTER 11 FACILITIES AND EQUIPMENT

TEST YOUR FOOD SAFETY

1. True or False: A food premise should be designed to have food flow in one direction only. (*See Premises Design and Layout, page 136*)

2. True or False: Walls should be dark coloured to minimize the need to repaint (*See Walls and Ceilings, page 139*)

3. True or False: Soft wood is a better choice for cutting boards than hard wood. (*See Cutting Boards, page 141*)

4. True or False: Ventilation means opening doors and windows to let fresh air into a kitchen. (*See Ventilation, page 145*)

5. True or False: Restrooms should not be shared by employees and customers. (*See Restrooms, page 139*)

Facilities Planning

Facilities design and equipment are fundamental components to a food safety system. Facilities that are planned according to sanitary design principles not only improve the efficiency of your operation, they reduce the likelihood of cross-contamination. In this chapter you will learn how characteristics like site location, floor-plans and construction materials affect your ability to supply safe food to your customers.

Location

Sites for food premises have to be chosen carefully. They must be free from conditions that can interfere with sanitary operation. Contamination comes in many forms like excessive dust, foul odours, and airborne microbes or chemicals. For this reason, sites must be set reasonably far from incompatible processing facilities or waste disposal facilities. The minimum recommended set-back is 30 meters from a potential source of contamination.

Premises Design and Layout

A properly designed food service premises will minimize the chance that food becomes contaminated. The *layout* should be designed to ensure that food only flows in one direction.

- Food should progress easily through receiving to storage, to preparation, to packaging and/or serving with as little handling as possible.

- Foot traffic should be controlled as much as possible to minimize contamination of food.

LEARNING OBJECTIVES

After completing this chapter, you should be able to:

- Describe a well-designed restaurant.
- Select proper equipment.
- Review utilities, lighting and ventilation.
- Arrange for careful handling of garbage and solid waste.

TERMS TO KNOW

Air Gap: An air space separating a water supply outlet from any potentially contaminated source.

Back Siphonage: A type of backflow that occurs when a loss of pressure in the water supply causes dirty water or chemicals to be sucked back into the drinkable water supply.

Backflow: A reverse flow of unsafe water into sinks and equipment.

Cleanable: Surfaces are accessible and soil and waste can be effectively removed by normal cleaning methods.

Coving: A curved, sealed edge between the wall and the floor.

Cross-Connection: A physical link through which contaminants from drains, sewers, or waste-water can enter a potable water supply.

Layout: The order of equipment, work areas and furniture for dining and back-of-the house areas.

Lux: The International System of Units of illumination.

Workflow: The order of the tasks in preparing a food item, beginning in the receiving area and leading to the dining room.

Workplace Hazardous Materials Information System (WHMIS): An information system designed to protect the health and safety of employees involved in the purchase, storage or use of potentially hazardous chemicals.

- Keep non-food preparation areas or processes, like chemical storage or waste containment, far away from food preparation areas.

- Only choose construction materials that are easy to clean and maintain.

- Include storage areas in your plan. There should be enough to accommodate all your food and non-food operating materials.

Choosing the right layout for your business is important. Applications for new operating permits and permit renewals require the co-operation of a number of regulatory authorities. Local and/or provincial health agencies usually require the submission of building plans, seating capacity, fire permits, retail business and liquor licenses, and menu outlines if applicable. Other considerations include zoning restrictions and waste disposal. Contact your local business service centre and Public Health Unit for guidelines.

Workflow Patterns

Workflow refers to the order of tasks required to prepare a food item, beginning in the receiving area and leading to the dining room. The goal in designing a floor plan is to control safety and quality at all critical points while keeping your production costs as low as possible. Keep the following principles in mind:

- Plan tasks so employees travel the shortest distance in the least time.

- Arrange tasks so employees do not criss-cross the work area or backtrack. Avoid difficult patterns that can cause falls, collisions and spills.

- Have workspaces for preparing raw meats separate from workspaces for preparing ready-to-eat foods to avoid cross-contamination.

- Minimize trips to storage. Bring out food when needed, prepare it, and serve, hold or return it to storage for later use.

- Have workspaces and equipment ready when food is brought out of storage. Complete the task, move the food to the next step, and clean and put away the equipment.

Construction Considerations for Specific Areas

Storage Areas

Stored items must be protected from contaminants such as water leakage, pest infestation and any other unsanitary conditions. Separation of food and equipment from toxic and soiled material ensures that the opportunity for cross-contamination is minimized.

- Floors must be durable, easily cleaned and non-slip. Use materials that do not absorb water or organic material.

- Walls should be constructed of materials that are easily cleaned.

- The wall to floor joints must be coved with a gap no greater than 1 mm.

- Shelves and tabletops should be corrosion-resistant metals (still cleanable after repeated contact with food, water and cleaning compounds). Bare, unsealed wood is not an appropriate material. Shelves should be slatted and wide enough to avoid overcrowding and loss of air circulation.

- Adequate shelving should be supplied so that all materials may be stored off the floor. Shelf racks should be at least 15 cm (6 inches) off the floor. Avoid using bread racks or wooden pallets as these often lead to santitation and pest problems.

- Shelving should be at least 5 cm (2 inches) away from the wall to allow for easy access, cleaning and visual inspection.

- Bins for dry ingredients should be corrosion-resistant metal or food-grade plastic. Covers should keep out pests and moisture. Label bins with contents and use-by dates.

- Non-food items like chemicals must be stored away from food and any material that may come in contact with food, like utensils, linen or equipment.

- The personal belongings of staff must be stored in areas separate from food storage.

- Steam pipes, ventilation ducts, water lines and conduits should not be exposed.

Additional information on the storage of poisonous items can be found in *Workplace Hazardous Materials Information* (WHIMIS) guidelines (*For basic WHIMIS guidelines, see Appendix B*).

Restrooms

Restroom provisions, including plumbing provisions, are set by the National Building Code and regulated by local regulatory agencies. There should be separate restrooms for employees and customers. To keep food safe, customers must never pass through food preparation areas to get to or from restrooms. Restrooms should:

- Be completely enclosed and provided with a tight-fitting and self-closing door, with the exception of those washrooms designed for use by handicapped persons. They should never open into a food preparation or food storage area.

- Be equipped with a handwash station supplied with hot and cold water.

- Be equipped with toilet paper, soap and single-use disposable towels, or air-blowing hand dryers. Common towels are not allowed.

- Be equipped with a garbage can for disposable paper towels and a separate one for feminine sanitary products.

- Have handwashing notices prominently displayed in both public and staff restrooms.

Walls and Ceilings

Wall and ceiling construction in food preparation, processing and storage areas should be finished in tile, plaster, sealed brick, stainless steel or other equivalent materials that are smooth, impermeable and light coloured.

These materials are easier to clean and therefore are more likely to be kept clean. A light-coloured finish aids in the even distribution of light and the detection of unclean conditions.

It is recommended that ceilings be constructed from *cleanable* sound-absorbing materials such as smooth, sealed plaster, tiles or panels. Studs, joists, rafters and pipes should not be exposed in the dining area unless they are finished and sealed for easy cleaning. In addition, inserts for false ceilings must be non-porous in food preparation and storage areas.

Flooring

Flooring should be able to withstand the shock of constant traffic and items being dropped. Floors that are subject to moisture must be constructed of impervious materials and sloped to allow draining. A minimum slope of 2% is recommended.

FIGURE 11.0 Coving

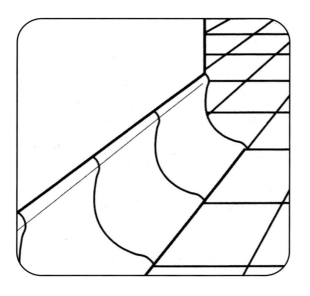

Kitchen, Storage and Work Area Flooring

- Use materials that are durable, easy to clean and non-slip such as epoxy resin and tile.

- Floors should be kept clean. Replace or repair all cracked or chipped flooring.

- Floor joints should be coved at the wall and sealed. *Coving* is a curved, sealed edge between the wall and the floor. It removes sharp corners and gaps that make cleaning difficult (*See Figure 11.0*).

Dining Areas

Carpeting is only allowed in dining rooms or public areas. Choose carpeting with a tight weave for easy cleaning. Carpets should be vacuumed daily and shampooed regularly.

Food Preparation and Storage Equipment

The Standards Council of Canada (SCC) coordinates voluntary standardization and Canada's participation in international standardization. Check equipment evaluations published by: the NSF International, formerly the National Sanitation Foundation; Underwriters Laboratories, Inc., (UL); the Canadian Standards Association; and, the SCC. Look for CSA, NSF and UL and ULC seals.

Choose only equipment that meets industry and regulatory standards. Never use equipment intended for the home in commercial operations.

Food Contact Surfaces

Food contact surfaces and food splash surfaces must be constructed in a way that facilitates cleaning, sanitation and maintenance. They must be smooth and non-absorbent to eliminate the possibility that they harbour micro-organisms or other contaminants.

The following specifications include equipment food contact surfaces. All surfaces must be:

- Easy to reach and cleanable by normal methods.

- Non-toxic, non-absorbent, corrosion-resistant, and non-reactive with food or cleaning products. They should never transfer colour, odour or taste to food.

- Free of pits, crevices, sharp internal angles, inside threads and shoulders, ledges and rivet heads.

- Free from breaks, cracks or other imperfections that might impede cleaning and sanitizing and be finished with smooth welds and joints.

Equipment must use only non-toxic lubricants and have rounded, tightly sealed corners and edges. Solid and liquid waste traps must be easy to remove. For example, drink dispensers should have trays that are easy to remove without tools for cleaning or repair.

Wood is not normally acceptable as a food contact surface. Exceptions are made in the case of hard maple or other hard, close-grained wood which may be used for cutting boards and blocks, rolling pins, doughnut dowels, salad bowls, and chopsticks.

Cutting Boards

Wash, rinse and sanitize cutting boards before and after each use, after changing the food being prepared, and after interruption. Cutting boards that are used continuously must be washed, rinsed and sanitized at least every four hours.

- Food-grade, seamless, hard rubber or acrylic blocks are safer and are required in some areas. These boards can be cleaned and sanitized in a three-compartment sink or a dishwasher. Those that are too large to move must also be cleaned and sanitized in place.

- If wooden cutting boards are used, choose those made from seamless non-toxic hardwoods such as maple or birch.

- Be aware that bacteria can survive and grow in the cuts and scratches on wooden and plastic cutting boards. It is recommended that cutting boards be replaced or resurfaced on a regular basis or when the board can no longer be effectively cleaned.

Refrigerators and Freezers

The types of foodservice refrigerators and freezers include walk-ins and reach-ins, under the counter units, open units and display units. Avoid overcrowding shelves to ensure proper cooling temperatures are maintained. All equipment used for refrigeration or cooling must be equipped with thermometers that are easy to read and accurate to ± 1°C (± 2°F) and that are calibrated on a regular basis.

Cook-Chill Equipment

Cook-chill equipment is designed to rapidly cool and then reheat foods. Large scale foodservice operations most often use this type of equipment.

Blast Chillers

These units look like refrigerators and freezers with control panels. Blast chillers chill foods from 60°C to 2°C (140°F to 36°F) in 90 minutes or less. Each unit should have an alarm or signal indicating the end of the chilling cycle.

DID YOU KNOW?

Some manufacturers make coloured cutting boards to help minimize the risk of cross-contamination. Colour coding tells employees which equipment to use with what products, such as green for produce, yellow for chicken and red for meat.

Tumbler Chillers

These units have automated systems that combine steam-jacketed kettles, pump/filler stations, conveyors, and cooking and chilling tanks. Tumbler chillers are often used with liquid or thick foods and can serve as reheating units.

Warewashing Machines

Warewashing machines are complex systems that use large volumes of water during operation. There are two common types used in commercial foodservice: high-temperature and chemical-sanitizing. High-temperature machines use hot water for sanitation of soiled wares, whereas chemical-sanitizing units are known as "low temperature" machines which use chemical agents.

Location and Set-Up

• The distance water has to be piped from the water source to dishwasher should be as short as possible to prevent heat loss.

• The unit should be raised at least 15 cm (6 inches) off the floor for easy cleaning.

• The unit should include an easy to read water pressure measuring device and temperature thermometer. Look for machines with readable data plates affixed by the manufacturer indicating the design and operating specifications.

• Follow manufacturer instructions for proper sanitizing. Post instructions stating the water temperature, conveyor speed, water pressure settings, and the amount and concentration of detergent required for use near the machine.

• Make sure that staff are trained in the use and maintenance of the machines.

Clean in Place Equipment (CIP)

"Clean in Place" equipment is constructed so that detergent, hot water rinse and sanitizing solutions circulate through a fixed system. The system is self-draining and must be inspected regularly to ensure that all interior food contact surfaces are effectively cleaned. Examples include soft-serve ice cream and frozen yogurt dispensers.

• Cleaning and sanitizing solutions must remain in the pipes for a fixed time period.

• All interior and exterior food contact surfaces must be cleaned.

• Washing, rinsing and sanitizing liquids must not leak into the rest of the machine and must drain completely.

• If not designed to be taken apart for cleaning, the machine must include a system, such as a removable panel, to check whether cleaning is complete.

Portable Equipment

This equipment makes cleaning easier and allows you to use a workspace for more than one purpose. Choose equipment that an employee can roll or pick up without requiring help.

Immobile Equipment

Follow the manufacturer's instructions for leaving space from the wall or between other pieces of equipment. Immobile counter-top equipment should be on legs that allow a 10 cm (4 inch) space or be sealed to the counter with non-toxic food-grade sealant.

Utilities

Your water supply and electrical service should support your cleaning program and never endanger food. All utility lines, as well as heating ducts, should be suspended away from work areas to prevent the risk of contamination. They should be constructed of material that resists erosion, rust or paint flaking and be insulated where appropriate to prevent condensation.

All lines should be clearly labelled and/or colour coded.

Lighting

Building codes require acceptable levels of lighting. One measurement of lighting is *lux*. Lux is the International System of Units of illumination. Lux is equal to one lumen per square metre, and equivalent to .0929 foot-candles. Approximately 50 foot-candles is equivalent to 540 lux.

The FRFSC states that unless otherwise specified, the minimum lighting intensities should be:

1) 110 lux in walk-in coolers, dry food storage areas, and in all other areas and rooms during periods of cleaning.

2) 220 lux in areas where fresh produce or packaged foods are sold or offered for consumption; areas used for handwashing, warewashing, and equipment and utensil storage; and in toilet rooms.

3) 540 lux where a food handler is working with unpackaged potentially hazardous food or with food utensils and equipment such as knives, slicers, grinders or saws where employee/worker safety is a factor.

• Design light fixtures to prevent the accumulation of dirt and to be easily cleanable.

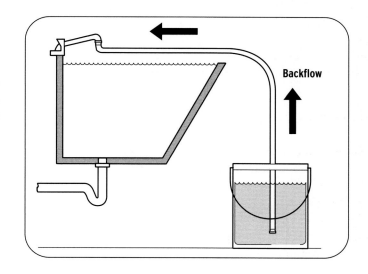

FIGURE 11.1 Common Cross-Connection

Backflow

THE USE OF NON-POTABLE WATER IN FOOD PREMISES IS PROHIBITED.

FIGURE 11.2 Air Gaps to Prevent Backflow

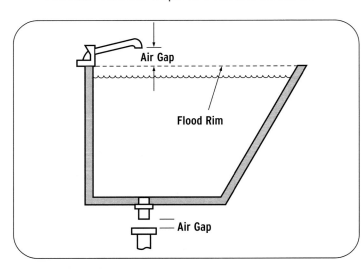

An air gap is a physical space between water that may be contaminated and the potable water source. Examples include the space between the water faucet and capacity rim of a sink, or the drain pipe of a sink and the floor drain beneath it.

- Lighting should be bright enough to reveal dirt and stains. It should be set to ensure the safe and sanitary production of food and facilitate cleaning of the premises.

- Light bulbs, heat lamps and infrared bulbs should be shielded with shatter-proof coverings so they cannot contaminate food in case they break.

Water Supply

Your water supply must be obtained from approved sources such as public water systems or private systems that meet public health requirements (*See Appendix A for a link to Health Canada's Water Quality website*). It must supply potable (drinkable) hot and cold water under adequate pressure and in sufficient quantities to meet peak demands during operation. Hot water must be of high enough temperature to effectively clean and sanitize.

- If your water is supplied by a private well, have it checked regularly by the local regulatory authority. You must have a written water sampling plan and protocol as part of your HACCP Prerequisite Program.

- If you use bottled water, it must be dispensed from its original container.

Plumbing

The plumbing system conveying water and waste requires the approval of local or provincial/territorial building authorities. A poorly designed plumbing system can lead to contamination of the potable water supply. *Cross-connections* (*See Figure 11.1*) and sewage *backflow* pose serious health hazards.

A plumbing cross-connection is most easily defined as any actual or potential connection between a potable and non-potable water supply or other substance (such as steam, gas, or chemical). When cross-connection safety devices are not installed, backflow or *back siphonage* can occur.

Backflow is the reverse flow of water, other liquids or substances from a source of potential contamination into the drinkable water system. Back-siphonage can occur when the pressure in the safe water supply drops to below the pressure of the unsafe water, sucking unsafe water into potable water.

To avoid cross-connections, backflow and back siphonage install backflow prevention devices, such as *air gaps* (*See Figure 11.2*) and vacuum breakers, wherever required and ensure that they are in compliance with the local plumbing and building codes.

Sewage

Sewage disposal systems must meet all local or provincial/territorial requirements. Keep sewage water and solids from contaminating food.

- All drains should be kept clear to prevent flooding.

- Any area where water is often spilled or that is cleaned by hosing down, such as a dishwashing area or kitchen, should have its own floor drain.

- All pipes containing non-drinkable water, such as those coming from toilets or sinks, should be identified by a plumber and labeled.

Ventilation

Ventilation removes steam, smoke, grease and heat from equipment and food-preparation areas, then replaces it with make-up air (clean air).

The air supplied to the food premises must be of sufficient quality that it does not contaminate the equipment or the food. Unclean air, excessive dust, odours or build-up of condensation or grease are all potential sources of food contamination. Build-up of constituents or residue in equipment such as range hoods also pose a fire hazard. Mechanical ventilation systems must meet local and provincial/territorial requirements.

Garbage Disposal & Waste Management

As a foodservice or food retail operator it is your responsibility to ensure that waste is managed in a safe manner and documented within your HACCP prerequisites.

"Garbage" in this section refers to any waste or refuse, including recyclable materials.

Solid and wet waste systems must meet all local or provincial/territorial requirements. Proper disposal is critical to preventing the spread of pathogens in food premises. Since garbage attracts pests both inside and outside a facility, disposal and maintenance of waste containers will minimize their presence.

Garbage disposal begins with keeping garbage away from food and food-contact surfaces.

- Remove garbage as soon as possible. At a minimum it must be removed daily. Garbage from other areas should not be carried through food-preparation areas.

MY WATER IS SUPPLIED BY

- Put garbage in containers that are durable, leak proof, easy to clean, and pest and waterproof. Containers may be metal or plastic and may be lined with plastic or wet-strength paper bags. Outside containers must have tight-fitting lids and be cleaned regularly.

- Provide enough containers and dumpsters to hold all garbage between pick ups. Store the containers on or above smooth surfaces that repel liquids, such as sealed concrete, in a cleanable, pest-free area away from food storage and preparation areas.

- Regularly clean and sanitize garbage storage rooms and containers. Use an area located away from food storage and preparation areas, that is equipped with hot and cold water, and a floor drain.

- Building codes require appropriate levels of lighting for different areas in your establishment. Lux is one measurement of lighting. Food service and food retail establishments must be built with appropriate lighting intensities.

Summary

- Facilities that are planned according to sanitary design principles improve the efficiency of your operation and reduce the likelihood of cross-contamination.

- Sites for food premises must be set-back at least 30 meters from potential sources of contamination like excessive dust, foul odours, airborne microbes, and chemicals.

- Workflow patterns should follow one direction and minimize foot traffic.

- Your establishment's construction and operation must meet local standards. Check with your local regulatory authority to make sure you are in compliance.

- Stored items must be protected from contaminants such as water leakage, pests, toxic and soiled materials, and storage areas must be constructed of easily cleanable materials.

- Restrooms should be located far from food preparation and storage areas. They should follow local, provincial and federal regulations for maintaining cleanliness and ensuring cross-contamination does not occur.

- Choose equipment that meets the required standards. Equipment includes all food contact surfaces, cutting boards, refrigerators and freezers, in addition to warewashing and other machines.

- All foodservice and food retail establishments must be designed to be easy to clean.

- Proper garbage storage and disposal is critical to preventing the spread of pathogens. Therefore, closely follow all regulations pertaining to keeping areas clean and sanitized.

- Water must be potable! All sources must meet local public health requirements. The potable supply must be protected from contamination by plumbing systems. Avoid cross-connections, backflow or back-siphonage. Install air gaps and vacuum breakers.

- Ensure adequate ventilation for your operation.

A DIFFICULT TO CLEAN ESTABLISHMENT WILL NOT BE WELL CLEANED.

Consider This....

The Downtown Bar & Grill had recently reopened under new ownership. The new manager had been working with public health officials to be sure the establishment met local standards and regulatory requirements. He knew there was still work to be done and was in the process of drawing up a maintenance checklist. One of the problems that needed attention was the glassware washing machine at the bar. The machine's wash cycle was working but the unit could not be used because the large amount of water released after each load did not drain properly. The blocked drain caused the water to pool underneath the washing machine. Drain cleaners had been used repeatedly without any improvement.

Several patrons of the Downtown Bar & Grill became ill shortly after having drinks containing ice. When interviewed, the patrons mentioned a chemical taste to their iced drinks.

An investigation of the ice-making machine revealed that the drain at the bottom of the ice bin shared piping with the glassware washing machine at the bar. When the ice cubes were removed, typical washing waste was found in the bin.

Why did the people become ill?
What should be done to correct the problem?

Answers can be found on page 203.

EXERCISE 11

1. **Cleanable facilities and equipment are those from which soil and waste can be regularly removed by:**
   - **a.** Hired professional cleaners.
   - **b.** Normal cleaning methods.
   - **c.** Closing for two days.
   - **d.** Only using strong chemicals.

2. **Floors in kitchen, storage and work areas should be:**
   - **a.** Carpeted to reduce noise.
   - **b.** Non-skid, able to withstand strong cleaners, and should repel liquids.
   - **c.** Washed only with cold water and mild detergent.
   - **d.** Lightly cleaned once a week.

3. **The safest materials for cutting boards are:**
   - **a.** Food-grade seamless hard rubber and acrylics.
   - **b.** Soft wood, such as pine and balsa.
   - **c.** Stainless steel.
   - **d.** Rigid types of cardboard.

4. **Surfaces in refrigerators and freezers should be:**
   - **a.** Kept damp to prevent dirt from sticking.
   - **b.** Able to absorb excess moisture.
   - **c.** Non-toxic and not leave a colour, odour or taste with food.
   - **d.** Painted with a lead-based paint.

5. **A cross-connection is the:**
   - **a.** Proper way to link two warewashing machines.
   - **b.** Link between a potable water supply and unsafe water.
   - **c.** Piping used in drink dispensers.
   - **d.** Piping used in most dishwashers.

6. **An air gap is the:**
   - **a.** Air space between an outlet of drinkable water from any potentially contaminated source.
   - **b.** Distance from a dishwasher sprayer to the dishes.
   - **c.** Width of a faucet opening.
   - **d.** Space under a piece of equipment and away from the wall.

7. **Which one of the following is a good ventilation practice?**
   - **a.** Open windows or doors.
   - **b.** Exhaust hoods over cooking equipment and dishwashers.
   - **c.** Loose-fitting, easily cleanable filters.
   - **d.** Air intakes close to exhaust fans.

8. **If you have more garbage than fits in your containers, you should:**
   - **a.** Carefully pile it next to and on top of the full containers.
   - **b.** Put it in the dry storage area.
   - **c.** Buy more containers at once.
   - **d.** Store it in the walk-in cooler.

Answers can be found on page 199.

TEST YOUR FOOD SAFETY

1. True or False: Biofilms are an effective way to prevent bacterial growth on food contact surfaces. (*See Cleaning and Sanitizing, page 149*)

2. True or False: Water softeners can be used to boost the effectiveness of cleaners and sanitizers. (*See Factors Affecting Your Cleaning Program, page 151*)

3. True or False: Heat can be used as effectively as chemicals to sanitize food contact surfaces. (*See Sanitizing, page 152*)

4. True or False: The storage area for cleaning supplies should be locked. (*See Cleaning Supplies, page 159*)

5. True or False: Chlorine solutions can be prepared up to 48 hours in advance. (*See Chlorine, page 153*)

Cleaning and Sanitizing

Once you have designed and set up your sanitary facility, it is important to keep it that way! A cleaned and sanitized operation reduces the chance of contamination. While the terms are often used interchangeably, cleaning and sanitizing refer to two different processes.

Cleaning is the process of removing food and other types of dirt and soil from surfaces. Removing residual particles of organic material is facilitated by chemical agents.

Sanitizing is the treatment of a clean surface with a chemical or physical agent (like heat) to reduce the number of micro-organisms to safe levels.

Sterilizing is the destruction of all micro-organisms and spores.

All food-contact surfaces must be cleaned, rinsed and sanitized:

- After each use.

- When you begin working with another type of food.

- Any time you are interrupted during a task. The tools or items you are working with may have become contaminated without your knowledge.

- At four hour intervals, minimum, if the items are in constant use at room temperature for the handling of potentially hazardous foods (eg. deli slicers).

Food contact surfaces of cooking equipment should be cleaned and sanitized at a frequency that prevents the accumulation of grease deposits and other residues. Incomplete cleaning/sanitizing encourages the development of a *biofilm*. A biofilm is a microcolony of bacteria that securely attaches itself to an inert surface.

LEARNING OBJECTIVES

After completing this chapter, you should be able to:

- Supervise cleaning and sanitizing throughout your operation.
- Ensure safe machine and manual warewashing.
- Provide safe storage for clean and sanitized items.
- Train employees to safely handle cleaning supplies, including hazardous materials.
- Organize, implement and monitor a cleaning program.

Biofilm: A microcolony of bacteria attached to a surface that is extremely difficult to remove or sanitize.

Chemical Sanitizing: The process of subjecting a food contact surface to a sanitizing solution for a specific period of time to kill or reduce the number of micro-organisms on that surface.

Chlorine: A commonly used sanitizer, effective against many micro-organisms.

Cleaning: The process of removing food and other types of dirt and soil from surfaces.

Heat Sanitizing: The use of high temperatures to remove micro-organisms from surfaces. With tableware, utensils or equipment, the most common method is to spray or submerge them in hot water.

Iodine and Iodophors: Broad spectrum disinfectant active against many micro-organisms.

Master Cleaning Schedule: A comprehensive chart that outlines cleaning duties and procedures.

Quaternary Ammonium Compounds (quats): A group of sanitizers all having the same basic chemical structure. Quats are generally non-toxic, non-corrosive and stable when exposed to heat, but may not kill certain types of organisms.

Sanitizing: The process of reducing the number of micro-organisms on a surface to safe levels.

Sterilizing: The destruction of all micro-organisms and spores.

Warewashing Machine: Includes dishwashers, glass washers, pan and pot washers.

Once formed, it provides bacteria with an ideal environment for growth while protecting them from changes in pH, temperature, chemical cleaners and sanitizers – making the bacteria extremely difficult to eliminate!

Factors Affecting Your Cleaning Program

Type of Soil

Food soil characteristics will affect the ability of a cleaner. Different types of soil require special cleaning agents. For example, fats and oils are difficult to remove and usually require an alkaline cleaner whereas sugar easily disolves in water.

Type of Surface

Surface composition influences effectiveness of cleaners and sanitizers. Stainless steel is a common material used in foodservice, however, prolonged use of strong acid cleaners combined with chlorine can lead to corrosion. In this case non-abrasive alkaline cleaners are recommended. Beware, glass can be etched by alkalines.

FIGURE 12.0 Factors That Influence Cleaning

Factor	Effect on cleaning process
Type of soil	Different types of soils, for example protein based (blood, egg), grease or oil (margarine, animal fat), water miscible (dissolved in water, flour, starches, drink stains), acid or alkaline (tea, dust, wine, fruit juice) require special cleaning methods.
Condition of soil	The condition of soil or stain affects how easily it can be removed. Dried or baked on stains will be more difficult to remove than soft, fresh stains.
Water quality	Hard water can cause scale or lime deposits to build up on equipment, requiring the use of lime removal cleaners.
Water temperature	The hotter the water the better the detergent dissolves and the more effectively it will clean.
Type of surface being cleaned	Different surfaces require different cleaning agents and methods.
Agitation or pressure	Scouring or scrubbing or agitation action is often needed to loosen soil.
Length of treatment	The longer the cleaning agent touches the surface, the better the cleaning.

Water Quality

Impurities found in your source water can drastically alter the effectiveness of a detergent or sanitizer. Minerals in water may tie up active ingredients in sanitizers, reducing their effectiveness. They can also separate out as scale. In areas where water is classified as "hard", water softeners should be used to boost the effectiveness of cleaners and sanitizers.

Water Temperature

The hotter the water, the better it dissolves materials, however it is important to consider that some soil, like protein, can set at high temperatures, and that some detergents, like chlorine, are ineffective at high temperatures.

Water pH

Water pH ranges generally from pH 6.5 to 8.5. This range is of no serious consequence to most detergents and sanitizers. However, highly alkaline or highly acidic water may require additional buffering agents because sanitizers are dramatically affected by the pH of the solution.

Cleaning

Cleaning Agents

Cleaning agents are chemical compounds intended to remove soil or mineral deposits. In general, cleaning agents must be effective, stable, non-corrosive and safe for employees to use. They can be divided into different categories such as:

Detergents: All detergents contain surfactants, substances that lessen surface tension between the detergent and the soiled surface, allowing the detergent to penetrate and loosen soil. Most detergents also use alkaline substances to break up soil. Mild alkaline detergents are used to remove fresh soil from walls, floors, ceilings, and most equipment and utensils. Strong alkaline detergents are used to cut through wax and grease, and aged, baked- or burnt-on soil.

Solvent/Alkaline Cleaners: Often called degreasers, solvent cleaners are alkaline detergents that include a grease dissolving agent. These cleaners work well on grill backsplashes, oven surfaces, and even grease stains on driveways. Solvent cleaners lose strength when diluted and are too costly to be regularly used on large areas.

FIGURE 12.1 Factors that Influence Chemical Sanitizers

Contact	Solution must contact items for the time specified by local regulations.
Selectivity	Quats, in particular may not kill all types of micro-organisms.
Concentration	Concentration below the legal minimum may not sanitize. Concentration above a certain level may leave a taste or odour, corrode metals or qualify as a health department violation. It is best to use a system that automatically properly dilutes sanitizers.
Temperature	13°C to 49°C (55°F to 120°F). Solutions at the lower end of this range last longer. Above this range, chlorine may corrode metals and both chlorine and iodine may evaporate.

Acid Cleaners: Acid cleaners are used when regular alkaline cleaners do not work. For example, they are used for scaling in dishwashing machines, rust stains in restrooms, and tarnish on copper and brass. They must always be used carefully and according to the manufacturer's instructions.

Abrasive Cleaners: These contain scouring agents that can be rubbed or scrubbed on hard-to-remove soils. These cleaners are often used on floors or baked- and burnt-on soils in pans. Abrasives may scratch surfaces, such as Plexiglas, plastic and stainless steel.

Always follow manufacturers' instructions carefully when using a chemical cleaning agent. Rinse thoroughly after use. If misused, they can be ineffective and even dangerous.

Sanitizing

Sanitizing reduces harmful micro-organisms found on a surface to safe levels. It is not a substitute for cleaning. Food contact surfaces must be cleaned and rinsed before they can be effectively sanitized because sanitizers cannot penetrate organic materials such as food soil.

Heat Sanitizing

In *heat sanitizing*, the temperature of food contact surfaces must reach at least 74°C (165°F) to kill most micro-organisms. The higher the heat, the shorter the time required to kill micro-organisms. The most common way to heat-sanitize is to immerse or spray tableware, utensils, or equipment with hot water. Use a thermometer to check the water temperature of items sanitized by immersion.

To check temperatures in *warewashing machines*:

- Attach temperature-sensitive labels or tape that changes colour when the appropriate temperature is reached.

- Attach paraffin tape that melts at the required temperature.

- Attach a high-temperature probe.

Chemical Sanitizing

Chemical sanitizing can be done in two ways: either by immersing a clean object in a specific concentration of sanitizing solution for a required period of time or by spraying, rinsing or swabbing the object with a specific concentration of sanitizing solution. All sanitizers are regulated by Health Canada, either through the Therapeutic Products Directorate (TPD) or Pest Management Regulatory Agency (PMRA):

- TPD regulates warewashing machine sanitizers and products that are labeled sanitizers but make no kill claims and are generally found in the back of the house.

- PMRA oversees drug identification number (DIN) registration and oversees products that make kill claims. Labels must state concentrations, effectiveness, directions for use, and possible health hazards.

The three most commonly used chemical sanitizers are: *chlorine*, iodine and *quaternary ammonium compounds* commonly referred to as quats. These sanitizers are widely used in the food industry because of their effectiveness, reasonable cost and ease of use.

Chlorine

Items must be cleaned and rinsed carefully before sanitizing with chlorine. Chlorine is incompatible with most other chemicals and should never be mixed with detergents. It should be noted that chlorine compounds can damage rubber and metals, such as pewter, stainless steel, aluminum and silver plate. Using too much of a chlorine-based solution may also leave an odour on dishes.
Chlorine is not stable and will lose strength quickly. Fresh solutions must be prepared frequently and have a maximum storage life of 24 hours. Chlorine is ineffective and dangerous at temperatures above 49°C (120°F). More information on chlorine can be found in *Appendix C*.

Iodine and Iodophors

Iodine and *iodophors* (a mixture of iodine and surfactant) are broad spectrum sanitizers. Iodine compounds should be used only in solutions with a pH of 5.0 or less, unless the manufacturer allows a higher limit. Iodophors have an effective temperature range of 24°C to 34°C (75°C to 93°F) and vaporize at 49°C (120°F). They can stain and discolour equipment, especially plastic.

Quaternary Ammonium Compounds (Quats)

Quats are non-corrosive, non-staining, and odourless. Quats work well in both acid and alkaline solutions and, if used correctly, are fairly easy on skin (*see Figure 12.2*). Quats may not work with all soaps and detergents.

Mineral deposits in hard water may make some bacteria harder for quats to remove. Therefore, use quats only in water with a hardness of 500 mg/L* or lower. Check local regulations to ensure that the chemical makeup of your solution will work with the water in your area.

Change all solution when it becomes soiled, leaves the proper temperature range, or falls below the required concentration.

*mg/L is equivalent to parts per million (ppm)

Machine Cleaning and Sanitizing

Warewashing machines can help your operation handle a high volume of washing. Machines sanitize using either heat or chemical means. Always operate according to manufacturers' instructions. Below are some general procedures to follow regardless of the type of warewashing machine you use.

General Procedures

- Check the cleanliness of machines regularly and clean each machine as often as needed; a minimum of once daily is recommended. Fill wash and rinse tanks with clean water. Detergent trays and spray nozzles should be clear of food or other objects.

- Flush, scrape or soak items before washing. Pre-soak items with dried-on food.

- Correctly load the dishwasher racks — never overload them. This increases efficiency and helps ensure one-pass washing. Use racks designed to expose all surfaces to the cleaning solution.

- Check temperature and pressure of water.

- Make sure that detergent and sanitizer dispensers are working properly. Check sanitizer concentration frequently with test kits/strips obtained from the supplier.

- Check all items as they are removed. Run soiled dishes through again. Proper equipment and procedures will help ensure one-pass washing.

- Air dry all items. Do not use towels.

- Keep machines in good repair.

High Temperature Machines

These machines rely on hot water to clean and sanitize tableware, utensils and equipment. They must have a built-in thermometer to measure temperature at the manifold, where the water sprays into the cleaning chamber.

In the final sanitizing rinse, dishware must be exposed to clean rinse water for at least 10 seconds at temperatures of:

- 74°C (165°F) for single tank, stationary rack, single temperature machines.

- 82°C (180°F) for all other machines.

You may need to add a booster heater to your water system to provide enough hot water to reach required temperatures.

Chemical Sanitizing Machines

These machines use chemicals to sanitize and they generally require water temperatures from 13°C to 49°C (55°F to 120°F). Temperature used will depend on the chemical used. Choose a machine that automatically dispenses the chemical sanitizing solution into the final rinse water. Ensure that the proper concentration of the manufacturer- recommended chemical is used.

Manual Cleaning and Sanitizing

If you do not use a dishwashing machine, manual warewashing procedures may be used. Set up a two- or three-compartment sink away from food preparation areas (*see Figure 12.3*). Include an area for scraping and pre-rinsing scraps into garbage containers. Manual dishwashing equipment should have a thermometer capable of measuring up to 100°C (212°F) to measure water temperature, and testing equipment to determine the strength of sanitizing chemicals. Provide a separate drain board for sanitized items to be air dried.

FIGURE 12.2 General Guidelines for Chemical Sanitizers

	Chlorine	Iodine	Quaternary Ammonium
Minimum Concentration			
For Immersion	100 mg/L*▲	12.5 - 25.0 mg/L*	200 mg/L*
For Spray Cleaning	200 mg/L*▲	12.5 - 25.0 mg/L*	200 mg/L*
Temperature of Solution	machine - 13 - 49°C (55 - 120°F) manual - 45 - 49°C (113 - 120°F)	24°C (75°F) Iodine will leave solution at 49°C (120°F)	24°C (75°F)
Time for Sanitizing			45 seconds-2 minutes; some products require longer contact-time
For Immersion	2 minutes	2 minutes	
For Spray Cleaning	Follow manufacturer's instructions	Follow manufacturer's instructions	
pH (detergent residue raises pH of solution so rinse thoroughly first)	Optimum between 6.0 to 7.5. Dangerous below 4.0	Below 5.0	Most effective around 7.0, but varies with compound
Corrosiveness	Corrosive to some substances	Noncorrosive	Noncorrosive
Response to Organic Contaminants in Water	Quickly inactivated	Quickly inactivated	Not easily affected
Response to Hard Water	Not affected	Not affected	Some compounds inactivated-read label; hardness over 500mg/L is undesirable
Indication of Solution	Test kit required	Amber colour indicates presence. Use test kit to determine concentration	Test kit required; Closely follow label instruction

*Subject to variation based on manufacturer's compounds.
▲ Subject to variation based on temperature of solution.

FIGURE 12.3 Three-compartment Sink

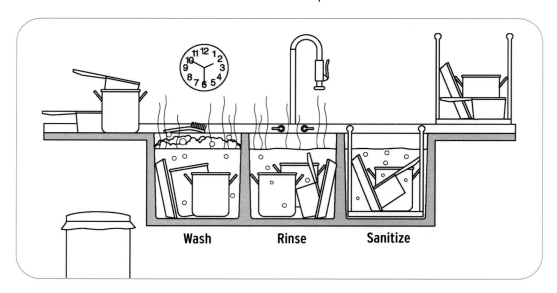

Wash   Rinse   Sanitize

Three-Compartment Sink

This method can be used on tableware, utensils and detachable equipment parts.

1. Clean and sanitize all sinks and work surfaces before washing dishes.

2. Flush, scrape or soak items before washing.

3. Wash items in the **first sink** in detergent solution at a minimum temperature of 45°C (113°F). Use a brush or cloth to loosen all remaining soil.

4. Rinse in the **second sink** in clear water at a minimun temperature of 45°C (113°F). Remove all traces of detergent.

5. Sanitize in the **third sink** by submerging items in either:

• Hot water at a minimum temperature of 77°C (171°F) for two minutes. To prevent burns, train employees to use tongs, a rack or basket to lower items into the water, or

• A chemical sanitizing solution at the proper temperature and mixed to specified concentrations for two minutes. Test the solution with a test kit.

6. Air dry all items.

FIGURE 12.4 Proper Cleaning, Rinsing and Sanitizing Temperatures

TEMPERATURE	PROCEDURE
13-49°C (55-120°F)	Range for chemical sanitizers to be effective
27-43°C (80-110°F)	Pre-wash cycle for high-temperature machine
45°C (113°F)	Wash-water temperature for manual immersion of tableware and equipment
45°C (113°F)	Rinse-water temperature for manual immersion of tableware and equipment
13-49°C (55-120°F)	Range for sanitizing (final) cycle in chemical sanitizing machines
66°C (151°F)	Wash cycle for multi-tank, conveyor and multi-temperature machines
71°C (160°F)	Wash solution for single-tank, conveyor and dual temperature machines
74°C (165°F)	Quickly kills most micro-organisms
74°C (165°F)	Rinse and sanitizing cycles for single-tank, stationary rack and single-temperature machines
77°C (171°F) for 2 mins	Heat sanitizing for manual immersion
82°C (180°F)	Final rinse and sanitizing cycles for a high-temperature machine at the manifold

Two-Compartment Sink

Some local health departments allow the use of two-compartment sinks, provided the second sink is large enough to permit complete immersion of items to be sanitized. Follow the same steps as for a three-compartment sink with the following changes:

1. Wash items in the **first sink** in detergent solution at a minimum temperature of 45°C (113°F), remembering to change water frequently. Use running water at a minimum temperature of 45°C (113°F) to rinse.
2. Sanitize in the **second sink** as outlined previously.

Cleaning and Sanitizing Equipment

Several types of equipment need special cleaning and sanitizing procedures.

Clean in Place Equipment (CIP)

This equipment is designed to have cleaning solution pumped through it. Follow the manufacturer's instructions. Cover food contact parts when they are not in use (*See Chapter 11*).

Fixed or Immobile Equipment

Follow the manufacturer's instructions for cleaning. Food contact surfaces usually require a different cleaning solution than non-food contact surfaces.

KEEP IT CLEAN

In my kitchen, we use _____ to clean and sanitize.

Train employees to:

- Turn off and unplug equipment.

- Remove food and soil around and under the unit.

- Remove detachable parts and manually wash them. Turn the blades away from their bodies and wipe away from sharp edges.

- Wash, rinse and sanitize the fixed food-contact surfaces. Wipe non-food contact parts with a sanitized cloth.

- Use marked buckets and separate cloths for food contact and non-food contact surfaces.

- Air dry all parts.

- Put the unit back together and tighten all parts and guards. Test the equipment at the recommended setting before returning settings to zero or "off".

- Re-sanitize food contact surfaces that were handled when putting the unit back together.

Spray cleaning may be used if allowed by the manufacturer. Spray each part with the required concentration spray for 2-3 minutes. Steam cleaning may also be used when the steam can be held within the item. Steam should be at least 93°C (200°F). Both spray and steam cleaning should be done so that food and food preparation areas are protected. Employees should be trained to use the equipment and wear proper protective gear.

Cooling and Microwave Units

The interiors of cooling and microwave units should be cleaned as often as necessary — at least daily — to remove spills, mould or odours.

- Clean shelves, walls, floors, door edges and gaskets on all units.

- Clean cooling units before shipments arrive. Move stored food to another unit during cleaning.

- Clean microwave units according to manufacturer's instructions.

Cleaning the Premises

Non-food contact surfaces such as walls, ceilings, floors, shelves and light fixtures should be cleaned at a frequency that will prevent the accumulation of dust, dirt, food residue and other debris. Do not let cleaning solutions or water touch food or remain standing on floors or shelves.

Cleaning Supplies

Janitorial tools should be cleaned and sanitized before being stored. They should be kept in a well lit, dry, locked area away from other chemicals, food, and items used to work on or prepare food. A service sink, equipped with a floor drain, should be conveniently located for cleaning mops or other wet floor cleaning tools and for disposing of mop water.

Cloths, Sponges and Scrubbing Pads

Cloths used for wiping food spills on food contact surfaces should not be used for other purposes, such as for cleaning spills of raw animal foods. Clean cloths, sponges and scrubbing pads regularly, and keep them in a container of sanitizing solution when not in active use. Air dry before storing in a manner that prevents re-contamination.

Brushes and Mops

Store brushes hanging, rather than on their bristles. Store dried mops hanging, rather than standing in buckets.

Floor Drains

Clean drains as the last task of the day, after other cleaning is done.

1. Remove the drain cover, remove waste and replace the cover.

2. Flush the drain with a hose or spray, without splashing.

3. Pour detergent into the drain, scrub or spray the drain cover, and rinse.

4. Pour a sanitizing or disinfecting solution into the drain.

Restrooms

Restrooms must be cleaned at least once every day and as often as needed to keep them sanitary. Implement a cleaning schedule requiring employees to check for trash and spills every hour. Refill soap, toilet paper and towel supplies before they are empty. Provide clearly written instructions for cleaning and sanitizing, listing all jobs.

Cleaning Tableware and Equipment

Store tableware, equipment and cleaning supplies in such a way that they remain clean and sanitary. Train employees to:

- Clean and sanitize drawers and shelves before clean items are stored.

- Clean and sanitize trays and carts used to carry clean dishes from the storage area.

- Store tableware at least 15 cm (6 inches) off the floor to protect from soil and condensation.

- Store glasses and cups upside down on a clean and sanitized surface or rack. Store utensils so co-workers can pick them up by the handles.

- Cover the food contact parts of stored CIP equipment.

Use of Hazardous Materials

Hazardous materials refers to any material that, because of its quantity, concentration, and physical or chemical characteristics, may be dangerous to human health or the environment. Hazardous materials include the following categories:

• Compressed Gases.

• Flammable and Combustible Materials.

• Oxydizing Materials.

• Poisonous and Infectious Materials.

• Corrosive Materials.

• Dangerously Reactive Materials.

According to Workplace Hazardous Materials Information System (WHMIS) regulations, employees must be trained to handle hazardous materials found in their workplace and supplied with the right equipment to perform the job. To help keep your employees and customers safe, use the following recommendations:

• Inventory all hazardous chemicals.

• Be sure all substances containing hazardous chemicals are labeled. Labels should state the name of the chemical, the hazard, and the name and address of the manufacturer or responsible party.

• Get a Material Safety Data Sheet (MSDS) for each hazardous chemical. Store this information in a "right-to-know" station, where employees can easily reach it (See *Appendix B*).

Now that you know what hazardous materials are used on your premises, make sure employees receive the following information:

• The common and chemical name of the product.

- Where and when the product is to be used.

- Proper training to use the product.

- Appropriate personal protective equipment (PPE) to wear when using the chemical, such as goggles, breathing masks, or gloves.

- Physical hazards, such as fire, toxicity or skin irritation.

- Health hazards associated with use of the product.

- Emergency procedures to take if exposed to hazardous chemicals.

- Protective steps in case of spills or leaks.

Once employees are trained to handle each chemical they work with and how to protect themselves during use, it is your responsibility to provide protective gear and to demonstrate appropriate emergency steps (*See Appendix B for more details on WHMIS*).

Organizing a Cleaning Program

Each foodservice & food retail operation needs an overall cleaning program to organize all cleaning and sanitizing tasks. Your program should help you identify your cleaning needs, select the supplies and tools you need, and train your employees to make the best use of their skills. Be sure to set up a *master cleaning schedule*. A master cleaning schedule includes:

- A list of items/areas to be cleaned.

- How the items/areas are to be cleaned.

- When the items are to be cleaned.

- What should be used to perform the cleaning.

- Who is responsible for the cleaning.

- Sign-off sheets verifying that the job has been completed.

To maximize the effectiveness of your program, it is important to remember the following:

- Supervise and monitor the cleaning program, and keep written records.

- Review the master schedule every time production, procedures or equipment changes.

- Conduct spot inspections to ensure that the program is being followed.

- Reward employees for a job well done, creating small incentives like monthly awards.

Summary

- Cleaning removes visible dirt and soil.

- Sanitizing reduces the microbial level to safe levels.

- All surfaces and equipment should be cleaned before they are sanitized.

- Surfaces can be sanitized with hot water at a temperature of at least 74°C (165°F) or by using a chemical sanitizing solution.

- Food contact surfaces should be cleaned and sanitized after every use, or after every four hours if in continuous use.

- All items should be air dried.

- Make sure your employees are well trained on how to use chemical sanitizers to avoid contamination and injury.

- Follow manufacturer's instructions.

- MSDS should be available and close to all the chemicals used in the establishment.

- Cleaning materials should be stored in a well-lit, locked room separate from food storage and preparation areas and clearly labeled.

Consider This....

A large university employs students to wash dishes for their cafeterias.
A team of students scraped every dish and utensil, placed them into the dishwasher rack and fed them into the high temperature dishwashing machine. When the wash and rinse cycles were complete an employee noticed that the dishes were spotted and still had bits of food on them. After checking the thermometer, the student discovered that the rinse cycle read 38°C (100°F), rather than the required 82°C (180°F).

The employee informed the manager and the dishwashing manufacturer was called. A service representative was dispatched to the cafeteria.

Are there risks to using these dishes?

What other methods can be used to clean
and sanitize the tableware until the machine is fixed?

Answers can be found on page 204.

EXERCISE 12

1. **Factors that do not influence cleaning include:**
   a. Soil type.
   b. Soil colour.
   c. Water temperature.
   d. Water hardness.

2. **Sanitize items in a three-compartment sink by using a chemical sanitizing solution or by:**
   a. Immersing them for 30 seconds in water that is at least 38°C (100°F).
   b. Air drying them after washing.
   c. Rubbing them with a towel.
   d. Immersing them for 2 minutes in water that is at least at 77°C (171°F).

3. **Dry sanitized items by:**
   a. Leaving them near an open window.
   b. Air drying them on a clean, sanitized drainboard.
   c. Rubbing them with a towel.
   d. Leaving them near a heat vent.

4. **In a three-compartment sink system for manual warewashing:**
   a. All sinks should contain detergent.
   b. All sinks should be at 93°C (200°F).
   c. Wash sinks should be at least 45°C (113°F).
   d. Wash sinks should be at least 82°C (180°F).

5. **Store cleaning supplies:**
   a. In the food preparation area.
   b. Outside or on the loading dock.
   c. In the dry storage area.
   d. Away from food and food contact items

6. **Store cleaning cloths, sponges and scrubbing pads:**
   a. In sanitizing solution or air dry them.
   b. On the floor under shelves.
   c. Hanging in the kitchen.
   d. In flatware drawers.

7. **A master cleaning schedule should list:**
   a. Outside cleaning firms to contact.
   b. Cleaning violations from local ordinances.
   c. The date of the next visit from the health department.
   d. Cleaning tasks, responsibilities, dates and methods.

8. **When spray cleaning with chlorine, the solution should be:**
   a. The same concentration as for immersion.
   b. 1/2 the concentration used for immersion.
   c. At the manufacturer's recommended concentration.
   d. You should not spray clean with sanitizer.

Answers can be found on page 199.

CHAPTER 13 PEST MANAGEMENT

1. True or False: Managers/operators should apply all pesticides themselves. (*See Pesticides, page 173*)

2. True or False: Refuse any shipment of supplies that contains cockroaches, cockroach egg cases, or mice. (*See General Preventive Practices, page 165*)

3. True or False: Rats need a hole only the size of a quarter to enter a building. (*See Building Grounds and Maintenance, page 166*)

4. True or False: Cockroaches harm food but do not carry diseases. (*See Cockroaches, page 168*)

5. True or False: Pesticide use is regulated by federal, provincial/territorial and local laws. (*See Pesticides, page 173*)

Integrated Pest Management (IPM)

Pests, such as insects, birds, mice and rats, pose a serious threat to public health and the environment. Pests damage food, supplies and facilities, but their greatest threat is that they spread diseases, including foodborne illnesses, by transferring micro-organisms to food and food contact surfaces. Physical contamination can also result when insect body parts, rodent hair, pest faeces and other debris falls into food. If not effectively controlled, pests can also have a negative financial impact on your business.

An *integrated pest management* (IPM) program is a dynamic program designed to prevent pests from infesting your establishment and to eliminate pests that are already present. In an IPM program, you work closely with a licensed *pest control operator* to safely use pest control methods. Four basic rules for developing an IPM program are:

1. Deny pests food, water and shelter by following good sanitation and housekeeping practices.

2. Keep pests out of the foodservice operation by pestproofing the building.

3. Work with a licensed pest control operator.

4. Educate employees about your IPM program and its elements, particularly sanitation. They should learn to recognize pests, their habits, and the conditions most likely to lead to an infestation.

Like many HACCP Prerequisite Programs, IPM strategies in food processing facilities involve steps for assessing risk, developing a management plan including physical and chemical controls, implementing the program, evaluating

LEARNING OBJECTIVES

After completing this chapter, you should be able to:

- Set up an integrated pest management (IPM) program.
- Use methods to keep pests out of the building and off the grounds.
- Select methods for detecting pests.
- Identify methods to control pests.
- Work with a pest control operator.

TERMS TO KNOW

Air Curtains/Doors: Units that put out a steady stream of air that flying insects avoid.

Contact Spray: Used on groups of insects, this spray must come in contact with the insect.

Fly Fans: *See air curtains.*

Glue Boards: Cardboard containers open at both ends that are used to catch pests. The glue on the floor of the trap hold roaches or rodents that enter the trap.

Infestation: A situation when pests overrun or inhabit an establishment in large numbers.

Integrated Pest Management (IPM): A decision-making process that uses control measures to prevent pests from entering your facility and eliminate existing pest infestations in an effective, economic and environmentally sound matter.

Pest Control Operator: A licensed or certified technician who implements and monitors control programs for companies that contract for services.

Pesticide: A product that controls, destroys or inhibits the activity of pests.

Residual Spray: A spray which insects absorb as they come into contact with it.

its effectiveness, and adjustment if necessary. Current, up-to-date written procedures for all aspects of the program should be kept in your establishment.

Preventing Pest Infestations

A regular cleaning and sanitation program, as described in *Chapter 12*, is your first line of defence against pests. By using a broad-based approach to IPM, pests can be managed without relying on pesticides.

General Preventive Practices

The best method for pest control is preventing them from entering your facilities in the first place. Start with these measures to keep all types of pests out of your restaurant:

• Use reputable and reliable suppliers. Check all supplies before they enter your building. Refuse any shipment in which you find pests, such as cockroaches, egg cases or rodents.

• Remove garbage quickly and properly. Keep garbage tightly covered so it does not attract pests.

• Store recyclables as far from your building as municipal by-laws allow.

• Store food and supplies properly and as quickly as possible after receiving.

- Keep all food, food products and supplies at least 15 cm (6 inches) off the floor and away from walls.

- Low humidity helps keep cockroach eggs from hatching.

- Refrigerate foods such as cocoa, powdered milk, and nuts, that attract insects after they are opened.

- Use FIFO (First In, First Out) to disturb insect breeding cycles and to prevent pests from settling.

- Use dehumidifiers and ventilation equipment that force air outside the building.

- Thoroughly clean and sanitize your premise.

- Immediately clean up all spills, including crumbs and scraps.

- Train employees to keep the break area and locker room clean. Food and dirty clothes should not be kept in or under lockers.

- Keep toilets and restrooms cleaned and sanitized.

- Keep cleaning equipment dry.

Building and Grounds Maintenance

Pests are attracted to damp, dark places. Holes and cracks, especially in older buildings, allow pests to enter and hide. A first line of defence is to eliminate easy entry points. Mice can squeeze through cracks the size of a dime, while rats can enter through a quarter-sized hole. Maintaining, repairing and remodeling your building can reduce pest control costs.

Doors, Windows and Vents

- All openings should close tightly, be kept closed except when in use, and checked as part of a regular cleaning schedule. Weatherstrip doors and windows.

FIGURE 13.1 Proper Sealing Around Pipes

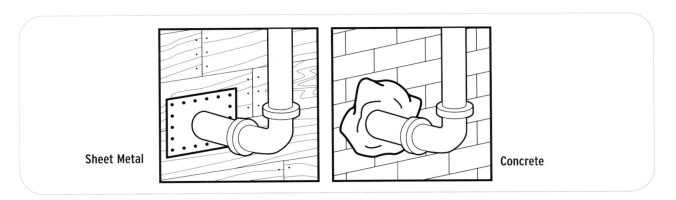

Sheet Metal

Concrete

- Use screening at least 16 mesh per square inch in windows and vents.

- Install self-closing devices and door sweeps.

- Repair gaps and cracks in doorframes and thresholds.

- When necessary, install *air curtains* (also called *air doors* or *fly fans*). These barrier devices emit a steady stream of air that flying insects avoid.

Pipes

- Use concrete or sheet metal to fill or cover all holes around or near pipes (*See Figure 13.1*).

- Install fine mesh screening over ventilation pipes on the roof.

Floors and Walls

- Seal all cracks in floors and walls. Use sealants recommended by your pest control operator, health department, or building contractor.

- Paint a white stripe around the edge of storeroom floors 15 cm (6 inches) from the wall. The stripe will remind employees to stack supplies away from the walls. Rodent hairs, tracks or droppings will show up against the white mark.

- Cover basement drains with holed, hinged metal caps to keep out rats and to make cleaning easier.

Indoor Garbage Storage Areas

To prevent odours and spills that attract pests:

- Keep garbage in sealed plastic bags inside tightly covered containers.

- Regularly wash, rinse and sanitize the containers.

Grounds and Outdoor Serving Areas

Keeping areas around the building clean will help prevent pests from entering your establishment. To keep areas near the building pest-free:

- Block, seal or caulk cracks and crevices around foundations and access points to wall cavities.

- Keep lawn tidy, get rid of standing water, and remove all litter and pet waste. Do not store building materials, old equipment, or any waste materials outside for any length of time.

To avoid attracting bees, wasps and other insects:

- Cover all outdoor garbage containers and dumpsters.

- Remove dirty dishes and uneaten food from tables and quickly clean up spills.

- Avoid serving canned drinks outdoors. Bees and wasps often crawl inside the cans and may sting the drinker.

- Allow only your pest control operator — not your employees — to remove hives and nests. These tasks take skill and are dangerous.

- Keep insect zappers away from building doors, serving areas, food, employees and customers. Use zappers that stun insects, then trap them on glue paper.

- Do not allow employees or customers to feed birds on the grounds.

Spotting Signs of Pests

Even if you have a good pest control program, pests may still get into your building. Know how to spot signs of pests and indentify what kind they are. Record the time, date and location of any sightings and report them to your pest control operator. Begin corrective action as soon as possible.

Cockroaches

More than 3,500 cockroach species exist worldwide. Cockroaches often carry disease causing micro-organisms, such as *salmonella*, fungi, parasite eggs and viruses. Roach populations thrive in areas where food, water, and shelter are readily available. Focus preventative measures on dark, warm, moist and hard to clean areas, such as:

- Behind refrigerators, freezers and stoves.

- In sink and floor drains.

- In gaps around hot water pipes.

- In the motors of electrical equipment.

- Under shelf liners and wallpaper.

- Under rubber mats in beverage dispensers.

- In delivery boxes and bags.

- Behind walls and floor (especially rubber-based) coving.

A cockroach seen in daylight can be a sign of a major *infestation* because they normally search for food and water in the dark. Only the weakest members come out in the daylight. Cockroaches prefer carbohydrates, proteins and fats, but will feed on almost anything when hungry. If you suspect you have a cockroach problem check for these signs:

- A strong oily odour.

- Feces, which look like large grains of pepper.

- Egg cases which may be brown, dark brown, dark red or black and capsule shaped.

Use *glue boards* to monitor roach populations and locations. Glue boards are cardboard containers open at both ends. Glue on the floor of the trap holds cockroaches that enter. Set traps where three surfaces meet, such as on the floor in a corner. Check the trap after 24 hours and show it to your pest control operator.

Flies

The common housefly is a greater threat to human health than the cockroach. Flies transmit several foodborne illnesses such as *Shigellosis* because they feed on garbage and animal wastes. They spread bacteria with their eggs, mouths, feet, hair, feces and vomit. Flies have no teeth and eat only liquid or food they have dissolved. Flies generally:

- Can enter a building through an opening the size of a pinhead.

- Are drawn to odours of decay, garbage, and waste to lay their eggs. They prefer areas sheltered from wind.

- Need moist, warm, decaying material protected from sunlight for their eggs to hatch into maggots. In warm summer weather, flies rapidly reproduce and maggots may grow into adult flies in six days.

Other Insect Pests

Beetles, moths and ants can survive on very small amounts of food. Flour moth larvae, beetles, and similar insects are found in dry storage areas. Signs of infestation include insect bodies, wings or webs, clumped-together food, and holes in food and packaging. Control these pests by storing food in tightly covered containers, using FIFO, and cleaning and sanitizing food preparation and serving areas.

Ants often nest in walls and floors, especially near stoves and hot water pipes. They are drawn to sugary foods, oils or greasy residue. Control ants by cleaning up all food scraps and spills. They will not cross sticky barriers – try laying down two-sided tape or gum resin barrier paste as a deterrent.

Rodents

Rodents, also called vermin, eat and ruin food and damage property. They are a serious health hazard. They can spread disease through their waste and by touching food or food contact surfaces. Rodents have a simple digestive system and weak bladder control. They urinate and defecate as they move about in your facility, and their waste can fall, be blown, or carried into food. Like other pests, they breed quickly and often.

Mice and rats can infest a building at the same time. Look for these signs of infestation:

Droppings: Fresh droppings are shiny and black. Older droppings are gray and dried.

Gnawing: Rats gnaw to reach food and to keep their teeth worn down. Rats can eat through pipes and hardened concrete as well as sacks, wood and cardboard.

Tracks: Check dusty surfaces by shining a light across them from a low angle.

Nesting materials: Mice use scraps of paper, hair and other soft material.

Holes: Rats nest in burrows, usually in dirt, rock piles, or along foundations.

Call your pest control operator if you think you have mice or rats. Rats are smart enough to avoid poorly set traps and other control measures. Rat bites are very dangerous to humans, and dead rats must be carefully handled to avoid spreading disease.

Birds

Common pigeons, starlings and sparrows may nest in or near buildings. They eat animal and vegetable food items, and their droppings carry fungi that causes serious illness. Call your pest control operator to control birds. Your pest control operator has chemicals, electric shock equipment, netting and traps to drive away birds.

Take Corrective Action

If pests or any sign of pest infestation is found in your establishment, thoroughly clean and sanitize the food premises to eliminate pest harbourage.

- Discard all contaminated food as it is not fit for human consumption.

- Clean and sanitize food surfaces and surrounding areas to destroy microscopic pathogens.

- Implement control and eradication plans detailed in your IPM strategy.

Working with a Pest Control Operator

Hire a licensed, certified, and reputable pest control operator to handle pest control procedures. You should work with a pest control operator because:

1. Pest control operators use methods that combine sanitation, non-chemical means, building maintenance and chemical treatment.

2. Pest control operators know about new equipment and products.

3. Pest control operators provide emergency service to help solve problems right away.

Documentation

Pest control measures should be documented. Owners/operators should take note of information the pest control technician may need for follow up. Documentation should include:

- The name of the pest control operator.

- The chemicals used for pest control (including the concentrations and locations applied).

- The procedures and methods used.

- The frequency of application.

- A map of trap locations.

- Records of inspection and monitoring.

DID YOU KNOW?

Effective pest control programs are in place to prevent entry, detect and eliminate pests, and to prevent contamination of food!

Inspection

For an effective first inspection, you should walk around the building with the pest control operator and you should:

- Prepare employees to answer the pest control operator's questions.

- Have building plans and equipment diagrams available.

- Point out possible trouble spots.

Have the pest control operator outline in writing the treatment plan:

- Materials to be used.

- Dates and times of treatment.

- Steps you can take to control pests.

- Building defects that may cause problems.

Treatment Procedures

Find out exactly which chemicals and procedures will be used in specific areas. Require the pest control operator to outline any risks of planned treatments, products, and equipment. Train employees to know and avoid any hazards.

Treatment Preparation

The federal government requires a pest control operator to give you sufficient advance warning to properly prepare your facility for the visit.

Employees must be evacuated during the treatment.

Follow Up

Your pest control contract should mention follow-up visits after each treatment to review how well the treatment is working. You or your supervisors also should regularly check the restaurant and call the pest control operator if pests appear again.

Pest Control Operator Methods

To control pests, pest control operators use several methods in ways that do not endanger employees and customers. Methods which utilize the minimal amount of chemical control possible are highly encouraged.

Controlling Insects

Repellents

Repellents are liquids, powders and mists that keep insects away from an area but do not necessarily kill them. Repellents can be used in hard-to-reach places, such as behind wallboards and plaster. They are also used with glue boards, *contact sprays* and *residual sprays*.

Sprays

Sprays are often used to control cockroaches and flies. It is easy to improperly use and abuse these. For safety, all foods and food contact utensils must be removed from an area that will be sprayed. Immovable objects, such as counters and ovens, must be covered and then washed, rinsed and sanitized after the area is sprayed.

Residual sprays are used in cracks and crevices and leave a film of insecticide that insects absorb or pick up as they crawl across it.

Contact sprays are used on groups of insects, such as clusters of cockroaches in a corner or a nest of ants. To be effective, the spray must come into contact with the insect.

CAUTION!

A number of pest control methods, including pesticides, can be hazardous to humans if not used correctly. Hiring a licensed pest control operator to manage your program and apply pesticides is highly recommended.

Controlling Rodents

Rodents tend to re-use the same routes and runways. The pest control operator will choose the best method to clear the area.

Traps

Using traps is a slow but generally safe method of killing rodents. Spring traps use food items, such as peanut butter, as bait. Keep bait fresh! Set traps in areas identified as rodent runways and check them often. Carefully remove and dispose of dead rodents. If the trapped rodent is still alive, call your your pest control operator to remove it.

Glue Boards

Glue boards work for killing mice, but are usually not effective for killing rats. Boards do not contain poison and are safe to use. Mice get stuck to the board and die in several hours because of a lack of oxygen or water, or from exhaustion. Boards should be put near mouse runways and checked often. Immediately throw out boards and mice.

Poisons

Poisonous baits should ONLY be used by a licensed pest control operator with extreme caution. Poison is added to the bait food and put near rodent runways. Poisoned baits should only be placed outdoors where they cannot contaminate food or food contact items. Bait should be set outside every day for at least two weeks. The pest control operator may change the type of bait and its location until the poisoned baits work. Employees must be careful to keep well away from these baits.

Pesticides

Pesticides are products that control, destroy, or inhibit the activity of pests. However, chemical pesticides are not a substitute for good sanitation. They can be dangerous to food, employees and customers. They are toxic and hard to use. Only work with a licensed pest control operator. In 2006, Health Canada's Pest Management Regulatory Agency (PMRA) implemented a new Pest Control Products Act (PCPA). The new act is meant to protect human health and the environment, and supports pesticide risk reduction. All pesticides must be registered with the PMRA. A public registry is available on the PMRA website (*see Appendix A*) that allows access to detailed evaluation reports on approved pesticides. The new act also allows Health Canada to require mandatory incident reporting.

Summary

- Pests are a problem in an establishment not only because they damage goods but because they can carry and spread a variety of diseases.

- An integrated pest management program utilizes a combination of preventive and control measures to eliminate pests and to keep them from infesting your establishment.

- Preventive measures include denying pests access to the facility and eliminating the sources of shelter and food. This can be achieved by good construction of the establishment including air doors and a good sanitation program, as well as proper garbage disposal.

- Control measures include chemical and non-chemical methods of pest control.

- Most chemical pesticides are poisonous to humans and extreme caution must be taken.

- Only a licensed pest control operator should apply pesticides.

- Work with a licensed pest control operator to make your operation pest free.

Consider This....

Jeb's Tacos is located in downtown Toronto in an old building that used to be a laundromat. The building is in an historical area where there are many shops and restaurants. Jeb recently acquired extra space in the building and remodeled his restaurant as part of a reality show on the Food Network, changing his establishment from a quick-serve to a full service restaurant. During his remodel Jeb replaced the floors and ceilings, and constructed his new kitchen with materials and equipment that are easy to clean and sanitize. Jeb also developed a master cleaning schedule and checks to make sure that the remodeled facilities are cleaned. He then documents the effectiveness by conducting regular self-inspections.

As part of his written procedures Jeb has included activities such as:
- spills and grease are cleaned up immediately
- FIFO is used for all products
- metal racks are used to keep food six inches off of the floor and away from walls.

During his first self-inspection, Jeb found evidence of a rat infestation (stored food, rat droppings) behind sinks, in the vegetable storage area and near the garbage storage area.

What factors might have Jeb overlooked in his recent remodeling that could have led to the rat problem?

What should Jeb do to address the rat problem?

Answers can be found on page 205.

EXERCISE 13

1. **What can you do in storage areas to make rodent signs more visible?**
   a. Paint a white line on the floor 15 cm from the wall.
   b. Raise the humidity level.
   c. Leave the floor wet.
   d. Use a blue light bulb and dust the area.

2. **Where should you install insect zappers?**
   a. Near the customer entrances.
   b. By the dry storage area.
   c. Away from food and customers.
   d. Near buffet tables.

3. **Seeing a cockroach in daylight usually means that you have:**
   a. Very few cockroaches.
   b. A large infestation.
   c. No rodents.
   d. Low humidity.

4. **To prove that you do have cockroaches, you should:**
   a. Use a glue trap.
   b. Leave food on the counter.
   c. Leave on the lights.
   d. Spray pesticides near the refrigerator.

5. **Which of the following is true of rodents?**
   a. They leave contamination everywhere they go.
   b. They are weak and easy to handle.
   c. They breed slowly and in small numbers.
   d. They cannot detect odours.

6. **Which one of the following is true of pesticide use?**
   a. Applying them often can take the place of good sanitation.
   b. They are flammable and non-toxic to humans.
   c. Their use is regulated by law.
   d. Anyone can apply them in a restaurant.

7. **Which one of the following pest control methods keeps insects away but does not necessarily kill them?**
   a. Residual sprays.
   b. Repellents.
   c. Glue traps.
   d. Contact sprays.

8. **You should provide your pest control operator with:**
   a. Strict instructions not to talk to employees.
   b. Recommendations from other restaurant owners.
   c. Building plans and equipment diagrams.
   d. Advice on how to do their job.

Answers can be found on page 199.

CHAPTER 14 REGULATORY AGENCIES AND INSPECTIONS

TEST YOUR FOOD SAFETY

IQ

1. True or False: Almost every aspect of a foodservice operation is regulated. (*See Government Regulation of the Food Industry, page 176*)

2. True or False: Food handling is one of the areas covered in food safety regulations. (*See What is Inspected page 180*)

3. True or False: Provincial/territorial and local agencies have more control than federal agencies over a foodservice establishment's day-to-day operation. (*See Provincial/ Territorial and Local Regulatory Agencies, page 178*)

4. True or False: A Public Health Inspector's main role is to help employees clean and sanitize the foodservice operation. (*See What to Do During an Inspection, page 181*)

5. True or False: The more co-operative you are with the public health inspector, the more smoothly the inspection will proceed. (*See What to Do During an Inspection, page 181*)

Government Regulation of the Food Industry

Almost every aspect of a food operation is regulated by federal, provincial/territorial and municipal agencies. These agencies have adopted standards that ensure consumers receive safe, wholesome and quality food. The *regulations* involve several levels of government.

Federal Governance

This is the highest level of government in Canada. The health and safety of Canadians and the food supply is governed by many departments and agencies, including their partners:

- Health Canada.

- Public Health Agency of Canada.

- Canadian Food Inspection Agency.

- Agriculture and Agri-Food Canada.

- Fisheries and Oceans Canada.

- Industry Canada.

Canadian Food Inspection Agency (CFIA)

Created in April 1997, the CFIA is mandated to safeguard

LEARNING OBJECTIVES

After completing this chapter, you should be able to:

- Understand the roles of federal, provincial/territorial and municipal regulatory agencies.
- Prepare for various types of inspections.

- Work well with a public health inspector/environmental health officer.
- Record and make good use of inspection findings.

TERMS TO KNOW

Act: A statute passed by a legislative body usually at the provincial/territorial or federal level.

By-law: A law that is established by a local authority such as a town, county or municipality.

Code: A collection of written laws covering a specific subject matter. A code is not law.

Law: Rules and regulations established by federal, provincial/territorial and local authorities.

Public Health Inspector: Also know as an Environmental Health Officer, these are industry leaders committed to protecting and promoting the health of people and their communities by anticipating and preventing diseases and injuries due to biological, chemical or other hazards.

Regulation: Rules that are established to outline specific requirements. Often embodied in an "act".

Canada's food supply and the plants and animals upon which safe and high-quality food depend. To enforce food safety and nutritional quality standards established by Health Canada, the CFIA administers and enforces several *acts* (*See Figure 14.0*).

The CFIA is led by a president who reports to the Minister of Agriculture and Agri-Food. The CFIA employs highly-trained professionals and specialists, including inspectors, analysts, graders, veterinary inspectors and other officers needed to administer acts for which the agency is responsible.

Under the *Canadian Food Inspection Agency Act*, the Minister of Agriculture and Agri-Food is responsible for the management and direction of the Canadian Food Inspection Agency and its operations. The Minister reports directly to Parliament.

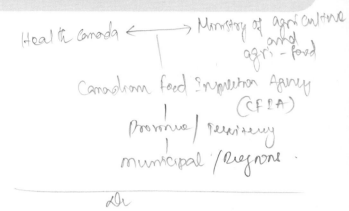

FIGURE 14.0 Federal Acts Enforced by the CFIA

- Agriculture and Agri-Food Administrative Monetary Penalties Act.

- Appropriation Acts.

- Canada Agricultural Products Act.

- Canadian Food Inspection Agency Act.

- Consumer Packaging and Labeling Act.

- Feeds Act.

- Fertilizers Act.

- Fish Inspection Act.

- Food and Drug Act (as it relates to food).

- Health of Animals Act.

- Meat Inspection Act.

- Organic Products Regulation.

- Plant Breeders Rights Act.

- Plant Protection Act.

- Seeds Act (as it relates to food).

Food Retail and Food Services Regulation and Code (FRFSRC):

Working through the Canadian Food Inspection System (CFIS) Implementation Group, government and industry have developed a model to regulate the practices of food service and food retail operators. This model is called the Food Retail and Food Services Regulation (FRFSR). They also developed an accompanying Food Retail and Food Services Code. Together, these documents are called the Food Retail and Food Services Regulation and Code. (FRFSRC).

The two documents provide a harmonized set of food safety standards and operational guidelines which are recognized by government, the food industry, and consumers.

The Code (FRFSC) consists of requirements for safeguarding public health and assuring food safety. It provides practical, user-friendly interpretations of the Regulations. The FRFSC is not intended to be a rigid, inflexible document. It should be used in conjunction with provincial/territorial regulations.

The FRFSC includes general information and guidelines to assist operators in the foodservice and food retail industries in the operation of their food premises. It also establishes universal learning outcomes that will help standardize food-handler educational courses and evaluation criteria.

Provincial/Territorial and Local Regulatory Agencies

Provincial /territorial and local agencies have the most influence on the daily operation of foodservice and food retail operations. These organizations provide interpretation and enforcement of the health regulations. By conducting food premises inspections, they determine if your food establishment is in compliance with those regulations. Agencies have the authority to test food for

STAY INFORMED...

It is the responsibility of the foodservice operator to know which legislation covers the service of food in their province/ territory and municipality. This is can easily be accomplished by:

1. Contacting your provincial/territorial agencies and local health units to ask for assistance. Many of the health units will provide information sessions regarding the role of health inspectors and legislation that relates to your location.

2. Making sure you have a plan to meet or exceed the regulations that are established. This will help to ensure the food you serve is safe.

safety and have it destroyed, if necessary. In addition, they may suspend your operating license.

Provincial and Territorial Governance

All provinces and territories have their own regulations for food premises. These are usually included in legislation called an "act". Regulations are developed to define intentions of the acts and contain minimum standards that must be followed by businesses and individuals in that area. Legislation passed by the province or territory gives local health departments power to enforce the CFIA and provincial/territorial acts.

For more information about provincial and territorial legislation see *Appendix A*.

Local, Regional and Municipal Governance

By-laws are created by municipal or regional governments to deal with important issues that fall under their jurisdiction. These issues encompass such things as smoking in restaurants, garbage storage and pick-up and mandatory recycling programs. Some municipalities, therefore, have food safety requirements that are different from provincial/territorial requirements.

In many cases it is the regional public health departments that conduct regular inspections, particularly in areas such as foodservice and food retail operations, where health hazards might exist.

Permit Applications

When considering building or renovating a foodservice or food retail establishment, operators are usually required to submit a copy of the plans to the local regulatory authority for approval. In some jurisdictions you may not be allowed to open or obtain an operating license prior to the approval of the health authority. Other regulatory agencies may also be involved to ensure compliance with the fire code, plumbing code and building code.

Variances

For special reasons, a regulatory agency may allow a restaurant to vary from the local food legislation. Variances are changes or suspensions of the rules for a specific procedure or part of the restaurant. Agencies grant variances only when they are certain that the restaurant's practices are based on scientific principles and will not lead to a health hazard.

A restaurant must follow the procedures set up by the local agency and make a written application for each variance.

If a variance is granted, the restaurant must comply with the new standards. Record-keeping must be revised and documentation regarding the effectiveness and safety of the new procedures kept. If a HACCP system is required, records should include CCPs, monitoring, corrective actions, and verification that the system is working.

The Inspection Process

A public heath inspector or environmental health officer, is trained to evaluate and monitor health and safety hazards and to develop strategies that control risk in the workplace.

They inspect restaurants, public facilities, industrial establishments, municipal water systems and other workplaces to ensure compliance with government regulations regarding:

- Sanitation.

- Pollution control.

- The handling and storage of hazardous substances.

- Workplace safety.

Periodic inspections of foodservice establishments are conducted to ensure they are in compliance with the

regulations. These inspections determine if you and your employees are preparing and serving food safely and in a sanitary environment.

The number of inspections conducted is based on risk assessments conducted by local regulatory agencies. The level of risk is based on the type of food prepared, if the food is prepared for people at high risk and the volume of food prepared. Complaints about an operation can also increase the number of inspections.

What Is Inspected

Remember, each province/territory has its own regulations and in many cases municipalities have additional by-laws regarding foodservice and food premises. Many common areas that are inspected include:

- Food source (obtained from approved suppliers).

- Food storage.

- Food handling (preparation, cooking and service).

- Potentially hazardous foods (meat, dairy products, eggs).

- Maintenance (garbage, equipment, facility).

- Personnel (facilities provided, attire, hygiene).

- Cleaning and sanitizing.

- Pest-control.

It is highly recommended that you get a copy of the regulations that apply to your area and make sure that you are in compliance.

DID YOU KNOW?

Public health inspectors may also be involved in the approval of plans for new facilities or renovations to existing food retail and foodservice operations.

What to Do During an Inspection

Health inspectors can conduct an inspection at any reasonable time during your operating hours and do not need to inform you that they are coming.

You should ask your health inspector for identification. Find out why the inspector is visiting. Is it a regular inspection or one in response to a complaint? Remember, the health inspector is working with you to ensure the food being served is safe for all consumers.

Be positive and professional in your dealings with the health inspector. Ask questions as you walk with them through the inspection so that there is mutual understanding of the observations.

During the inspection, you should:

- Co-operate. Answer all questions honestly and to the best of your ability. Make sure your employees know this and that they are comfortable answering the inspector's questions.

- Take notes. This shows you are serious about the observations and ensures that you have a detailed record of the visit.

- Correct problems on the spot, if possible - you will have less to do later.

- If you are unclear or think the health inspector may be mistaken regarding a variance, discuss it with them. If, after the visit, you need further clarification you can request it from the manager of the local health unit.

- Do not offer food or beverages at any time. This gesture can be interpreted as a bribe.

- Be ready to provide records. The public health inspector may also take swabs for bacterial testing and photographs or videos. You may ask why these items are required.

After the inspection, you should:

- Study your inspection report in detail. Discuss any areas of non-compliance and ask for recommendations so you can correct the problems. Write down any suggestions your health inspector makes so that you can implement them. You will be required to sign the report to acknowledge that you received it.

- Follow up by correcting each problem. Try to determine why it happened - for example, more training may be required, or equipment calibration may be needed. Whatever the reason, if you can determine why it happened you may be able to prevent it in the future.

- Make sure all non-compliance issues are corrected by the deadline provided. If you fail to do this you could be fined, be involved in court action and/or have your operating license suspended.

Finally, share the results of each inspection with your employees. Congratulate them on a job well done for their efforts in the areas where their performance was good. Identify the problem areas and provide help to correct them.

HEALTH INSPECTORS ARE THERE TO HELP.

Public health is a very important factor in the food industry. As managers/operators, your aim is to ensure your customers do not get sick. Health inspectors work with you to make sure that the health of your customers is not jeopardized - which could cause serious injury and cost you your business. View public health inspectors as coaches who give you advice on making your establishment the best it can be.

Summary

- Almost every aspect of a foodservice and food retail operation is regulated by federal, provincial/territorial or municipal (local) agencies.

- Each province/territory has a set of food safety regulations that operators must follow.

- Regions/municipalities also have a set of by-laws. It is important to know which legislation applies to your establishment.

- Establishments must follow standard food safety practices critical to the safety and quality of the food being served.

- The Food Retail and Food Services Regulation and Code (FRFSRC) consists of model requirements for safeguarding public health and assuring food safety.

- The manager/operator has to be aware of and follow the local standards.

- An inspection system lets the establishment know how well it is following good food-handling practices.

- Establishments should maintain high standards for sanitation and food safety and should use the health department inspections as a supplement to their self-inspections.

- Obtain a copy of the legislation that has authority in your area and make sure your establishment meets and goes beyond their requirements.

Consider This....

Peter, the certified public health inspector from Kitchener's public
health department, announced that he was there to inspect Gerry's restaurant,
the Greek Palace. Gerry greeted Peter and they walked into the kitchen together.
Peter pulled out a HACCP worksheet. Gerry explained that the cook was preparing
chicken souvlaki. Peter noted times and temperatures as he plotted them
on a time/temperature graph. Peter also filled in a product flow chart and noted the
CCPs for the dish. Gerry told Peter what corrective actions his employees
were trained to carry out if CCPs were not fulfilled.

Next Peter checked the concentration of the sanitizing solution in the three-compartment
sink that Gerry's dishwasher used for manually cleaning, rinsing and sanitizing
equipment. Peter also washed his hands in the food handlers' handwashing station.

Peter watched Gerry's staff for about 15 minutes, asking the cook,
salad prep and dishwasher questions.

Following the inspection, Gerry and Peter discussed the report. Gerry
compared his product flowchart for the souvlaki with the one that Peter completed
and made minor changes. Gerry and Peter chatted about a local hepatitis A outbreak
that affected one of Gerry's competitors. Peter emphasized the importance of
food handler hygiene, handwashing and a staff illness policy.

Did Gerry correctly handle the inspection?

What does Gerry need to do following this inspection?

Answers can be found on page 205.

EXERCISE 14

1. **Which one of the following must not obey food safety laws?**
   a. Food processors.
   b. Gardeners.
   c. Hot dog stands.
   d. Convenience store managers.

2. **Public Health Inspectors:**
   a. Clean floors, counters and dishes.
   b. Manage quick-service stores.
   c. Conduct inspections for the local health unit.
   d. Are trained to design thermometers and thermocouples.

3. **The frequency of inspections of a food establishment is based on:**
   a. The type of food prepared.
   b. The volume of food prepared.
   c. Who the food is prepared for.
   d. All of the above.

4. **On-site visits by the local public health inspector to check if a restaurant's food handling practices meet the local legislature are called:**
   a. Hearings.
   b. One-on-ones.
   c. Plan reviews.
   d. Operational inspections.

5. **What are some of the common areas inspected:**
   a. Pest-control.
   b. Food handling.
   c. Personnel.
   d. All of the above.

6. **When the public health inspector arrives for an inspection:**
   a. Walk with him or her during the inspection.
   b. Warn him or her that you expect fairness.
   c. Avoid talking with him or her more than necessary.
   d. Put him or her off until your work shift ends.

7. **During the inspection you should:**
   a. Offer the public health inspector food and drink.
   b. Answer questions and provide the requested records.
   c. Not allow employees to talk to the public health inspector.
   d. Allow the public health inspector only one hour for the inspection.

8. **If a restaurant does not meet the deadline for correcting violations a(n):**
   a. A restaurant may be fined or closed.
   b. An extension is automatically granted.
   c. A public health inspector will inspect the restaurant again the following year.
   d. A restaurant cannot hire more employees.

Answers can be found on page 199.

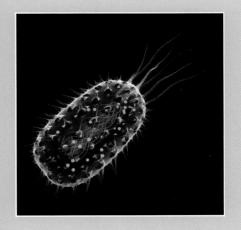

APPENDICES
PART
5.0

APPENDIX A

All provinces and territories in Canada have their own set of regulations for food retail and foodservice operators. These regulations are usually included in the province or terrritory's Public Health Acts. Regulations are developed to define the acts and provide minimum standards which must be followed by food retail and foodservice operators.

TrainCan, Inc. has developed ADVANCED.*fst*® using the highest standards set forth by Health Canada, the CFIA, FRFSRC and provincial regulations. It is highly recommended that food retail and foodservice operators obtain a copy of the regulations that apply to their area and ensure they are in compliance.

A detailed list of the different provinces/territories, their respective legislation and governing bodies can be found at: http://www.traincan.com and click on the provincial regulations tab.

BASIC WHMIS TRAINING

TrainCan is aware that WHMIS training is not part of the National Food Retail and Foodservices Code, and is not monitored by Public Health authorities conducting inspections. WHMIS is, however, federal legislation that is enforced across Canada by either Occupational Health and Safety officers or federal officers. It has been included in the reference guide because it may serve as a valuable addition to training.

WHMIS stands for:

Workplace **H**azardous **M**aterials **I**nformation **S**ystem

WHMIS is an information system designed to protect the health and safety of employees involved in the purchase, storage, or use of potentially hazardous chemicals.

Who is Affected by WHMIS?

Whether we realize it or not, we are constantly coming into contact with hazardous materials in the work environment. Anyone who purchases, stores, or uses any potentially hazardous chemicals, such as cleaning compounds or industrial chemicals, must have a working knowledge of WHMIS.

Under Canadian law and regulation, all workers must be trained in WHMIS, and training must be documented by the employer.

All workplaces and workers must comply with WHMIS. For example, WHMIS is enforced by the Ministry of Labour in Ontario under the *Occupational Health and Safety Act*. Similar legislation exists in all Canadian provinces.

If you have a good relationship with the suppliers of your potentially hazardous materials, it is not difficult to satisfy the legal requirements and to ensure the safety of employees.

THERE ARE FOUR MAIN COMPONENTS OF WHMIS:

1. SUPPLIER LABELS

Supplier labels are standardized and provide basic information on how to handle or use a controlled product safely. WHMIS information must be provided by the manufacturer or supplier of the product in both official languages, french and english. If a product is to be used in a workplace, it should be sold with a "hatched border". This border is on the original container's main label — a rectangular area outlined with a broken line around the perimeter — to draw the attention of anyone who handles the material. Products intended for the workplace and referred to as "commercial" or "industrial" products must display a WHMIS label.

Note: Retail products (items purchased in the grocery store or intended for home use by the general consumer) are exempt from WHMIS. However, since the use of retail products does not exempt the employer from the responsibility for proper training on use of the product as well as safety measures, many employers choose to specify that only WHMIS compliant products with Material Safety Data Sheets (MSDS) be used in their operations.

2. WORKPLACE LABELS

Labels must be applied to containers in the workplace when hazardous substances are transferred from their original containers. If a material is placed into a new container (such as a spray bottle), the new container must be labeled properly with the WHMIS information. This is so that WHMIS information is available to anyone using the material from the new container. Special "sticker" labels can be purchased from stationery suppliers for this purpose. The worker who transfers a product to a new container must consult the product's MSDS for information to be placed on the workplace label. It is a violation of the law to have chemicals available or stored in unlabeled containers.

3. MSDS (MATERIAL SAFETY DATA SHEETS)

Material Safety Data Sheets must be obtained from the suppliers of potentially hazardous materials, and must be made available to all workers in the workplace where the materials are stored or used. MSDS are provided upon request without charge.

A key element of WHMIS is that workers must be aware of relevant MSDS, and must be familiar with their contents. MSDS provide important information about chemical and physical characteristics, flammability and reactivity, safe handling practices, personal protection required, first aid, etc.

4. TRAINING

Training is an essential part of WHMIS compliance. All employees must regularly receive documented training on WHMIS as it applies to their work. For a food operator, this training would likely cover how to correctly use cleaning products as well as how to read MSDS and what procedure to follow in the event of an accident.

Note: It is the employer's responsibility to maintain a detailed inventory record of all potentially hazardous materials on site. The employer also needs to ensure that employees are properly trained on preventative and first-aid measures in case of emergency.

TEN STEPS TO IMPROVED SAFETY AND WHMIS COMPLIANCE

1. Consult your workplace health and safety committee about WHMIS.

2. Learn your legal rights and obligations under WHMIS. For details, refer to the Occupational Health and Safety Act in your province.

3. Confirm that your workplace purchases and uses chemicals that comply with WHMIS regulatory requirements.

4. Contact your chemical supplier for WHMIS information and for MSDS.

5. Carefully read supplier labels for all chemicals in your workplace. Get clarification if you do not understand WHMIS warnings or instructions.

6. Use workplace labels as required.

7. Learn how to read an MSDS. Consult the MSDS for chemicals in your workplace and follow the advice given in them.

8. Wear personal protective equipment, such as gloves and safety glasses, when recommended on an MSDS.

9. Follow label directions when using any potentially hazardous materials or disposing of empty containers.

10. Insist on regular WHMIS training for all workers. Promote WHMIS compliance by your co-workers.

HOW TO READ A WHMIS SUPPLIER LABEL

The Supplier Label is the label on the original container as provided by the manufacturer.

To be WHMIS compliant there must be a prominent "hatched box" on the supplier label containing the following 7 items:

1. **Product Identifier:** The brand name, code name or code number given to the product by its manufacturer; or the chemical name, common name, generic name, or trade name.

2. **Hazard Symbol(s) (if applicable):** The symbols that indicate general dangers such as compressed gas, flammable material, poisonous material, corrosive material, oxidizing material, etc.

3. **Risk Phrases:** Brief phrases that expand upon the danger represented by the hazardous symbols, for

example, "highly irritating to skin, eyes and nose".

4. **Precautionary Measures:** The specific measures which must be taken when handling or working in the presence of the product, for example "face shield and goggles required."

5. **First Aid Measures:** Phrases that indicate what is to be done to provide aid in an emergency to anyone exposed to the controlled product.

6. **Reference to the MSDS:** A statement on the label must indicate that an MSDS is available. This is a reminder that an MSDS should be consulted as it will have more detailed information.

7. **Supplier Identifier:** The name of the product manufacturer or importer must be stated.

An employer must keep records of all relevant MSDS and be able to prove that sheets have been made available to employees. An employer must be able to show that all workers have been informed about the proper handling and use of chemicals in the workplace. Workers are responsible for learning about hazardous materials in their workplace (through supplier labels and MSDS) and are responsible for working safely. Thus, safety in the workplace is a shared duty — employers and employees are both responsible to ensure that workplace materials are handled safely.

HOW TO READ A MATERIAL SAFETY DATA SHEET

There are 9 sections to an MSDS. Pay particular attention to sections 4 - 8.

SECTION 1: MATERIAL IDENTIFICATION AND USE
This section provides identifying information and must contain a telephone number that a worker or health professional can call to obtain more technical information about the product.

SECTION 2: HAZARDOUS INGREDIENTS
This section indicates the chemical components of the product that makes it a hazardous material. This must be interpreted by someone with technical training and a basic understanding of chemistry.

SECTION 3: PHYSICAL DATA
This section indicates the physical form, (solid, liquid, gas) and other physical and chemical properties, such as pH, specific gravity, colour, etc.

SECTION 4: INFORMATION REGARDING FIRE AND EXPLOSION HAZARD
This information will indicate the risk of the material catching on fire or exploding under certain conditions. This is very important information to be aware of.

SECTION 5: REACTIVITY DATA
This information is also critical and indicates, for example, whether a material is unstable, is reactive with air or water, or may pose a hazard through inadvertent or spontaneous chemical reaction.

SECTION 6: TOXICOLOGICAL DATA
This data indicates whether the material has been identified as a carcinogen, or as a material which is poisonous through some other mechanism. This section also contains information about safe exposure limits.

SECTION 7: PREVENTIVE MEASURES:
This section indicates what personal protective gear must be worn when handling the material, or indicates whether certain special practices are required for safety.

SECTION 8: FIRST AID MEASURES
These measures are summarized so that initial aid may be given to someone exposed to the product. The appropriate follow-up actions will also be given.

SECTION 9: PREPARATION DATA
The identity of the person or company which prepared the MSDS, and the date of issue is provided here. MSDS should be replaced with new issues at least every three years.

APPENDIX C

CHLORINE BLEACH AS A SANITIZER

Rating: Sanitizers must be EPA, or government registered at a specific concentration of available chlorine. Domestic, generic and distributor brand "bleach" is not intended as a sanitizer and is not registered or guaranteed at a specific level of concentration.

Availability: When chlorine is added to water, some of it combines with dissolved minerals and organic matter and is used up. Only "free" chlorine is available to fight bacteria, viruses and protozoa. Free chlorine levels can be measured using commercially available test kits. All measurements should be recorded in a log book.

Additives: Bleach products not specifically intended for use as a sanitizer often have additives, stabilizers and fragrances which make them unsuitable for food-contact surfaces.

Odour: While some associate the smell of bleach with cleanliness, a far greater number of people, especially in food service environments, find the odour offensive and unpleasant.

Efficacy: Chlorine is quickly inactivated by organic materials such as food particles and some detergents. Contact time is 2 minutes.

Stability: Exposure to air, light, and foreign materials can dissipate the levels of chlorine quickly, making it ineffective. Use in higher temperature water causes a high rate reaction that gives off chlorine (mustard) gas.

Corrosive: Chlorine is corrosive to items such as aluminum, stainless steels, as well as silver plating, rubbers and plastic finishes.

Concentration: Bleaches are unlikely to be dispensed or measured properly; effectiveness depends on the product's concentration in solution. Too little does not sanitize, while too much becomes highly corrosive.

Dangerous: Chlorine is highly reactive with many items that are used in kitchens, including acidic items such as vinegar and descaler. The result is a highly poisonous chlorine gas.

Price vs. Cost: While some believe that they can purchase bleaches inexpensively and do the job, the above factors, in conjunction with the amounts that people tend to pour out of the jug and have to replace to keep at the proper levels of concentration, can make it a more expensive choice than other methods of sanitizing.

GLOSSARY

A

Acidity: Measured on a pH scale from 0 (very acidic) to 14 (very alkaline [basic]), with 7.0 being neutral. A pH level between 4.6 and 7.0 will support bacterial growth.

Act: A statute passed by a legislative body usually at the provincial or federal level.

Air Curtains: Also called air doors or fly fans, are units that put out a steady stream of air that flying insects avoid.

Air Gap: An air space separating a water supply outlet from any potentially contaminated source. An example is the vertical distance between the rim of a sink and the faucet. An air gap is the only completely reliable method for preventing backflow.

Allergy: A condition of heightened sensitivity to certain things such as food.

Anaphylaxis: A severe allergic reaction that may result in death. It is induced by a repeat exposure to an allergen, sometime trace amounts, to which an individual is sensitized.

Aseptically Packaged: A system of packaging products in sterilized containers that is followed by hermetic sealing to prevent microbiological recontamination of the sterile product.

B

Back Siphonage: A type of backflow; occurs when a loss of pressure in the water supply causes dirty water or chemicals to be sucked back into the drinkable water supply.

Backflow: A reverse flow of unsafe water into sinks and equipment, posing the threat of contamination to food, food-contact surfaces, and safe water supplies.

Bacteria: Living single-celled organisms that are most often the cause of foodborne illness. Bacteria can be carried by water, wind, insects, plants, animals and people.

Bi-metallic Stemmed Thermometer: A common food industry thermometer that measures temperature through a metal stem with a sensor.

Biofilm: A microcolony of bacteria attached to a surface that is extremely difficult to remove or sanitize.

Biological Hazard: Contamination of food by micro-organisms such as bacteria, virus, moulds and fungi.

Biological Toxins: A poison that is produced by a plant or produced or ingested by an animal.

Blast Chiller: A unit that chills food from 60°C (140°F) to 2°C (37°F) in 90 minutes or less.

By-law: A law that is established by a local authority such as a town, county or municipality.

C

Calibration: The process of making sure a thermometer gives accurate readings by adjusting it to a known standard, such as the freezing point or boiling point of water.

Calibration Nut: The part of a bi-metallic thermometer that is adjusted to re-set the temperature during calibration. In digital thermometers this is usually a button.

Carrier: Someone who does not show any noticeable signs of being sick but carries micro-organisms that can be transferred to food or other people which can cause a foodborne illness.

Central Kitchen: A kitchen used to prepare food for large groups.

Chemical Hazard: The contamination of food by a variety of chemical substances normally found in establishments including toxic metals, pesticides and chemicals.

Chemical Sanitizing: The process of subjecting a food-contact surface to a sanitizing solution for a specific period of time to kill or reduce the number of micro-organisms on that surface.

Chlorine: A commonly used sanitizer. It is effective against many micro-organisms.

Ciguatera Poisoning: An illness that occurs after a person eats fish that have consumed the ciguatera toxin. This toxin occurs in certain fish such as amberjack, barracuda, grouper and snapper.

Clean: Free of visible soil and food waste.

Cleanable: Surfaces are accessible and soil and waste can be effectively removed by normal cleaning methods.

Cleaning: The process of removing food and other types of dirt and soil from a surface.

Cold-Holding Equipment: Equipment specifically designed to keep cold foods at a temperature of 4°C (40°F) or less. Includes refrigerated food bars, iced displays, refrigerated sandwich rails and insulated carriers.

Contact Spray: Used on groups of insects. To be effective, the spray must come into contact with the insect.

Contamination: The unintended presence of harmful substances or micro-organisms in food. Contamination may occur naturally, as in the case of toxins, or be introduced by humans or other sources.

Control Point (CP): Any step in the flow of food where a physical, chemical or biological hazard can be controlled.

Corrective Action: Action taken to correct an error or lapse in safe food-handling or HACCP procedures. For example, when the temperature of a hot food falls below 60°C (140°F), the proper corrective action is to reheat the food to 74°C (165°F) for fifteen seconds within two hours.

Coving: A curved, sealed edge between the wall and the floor.

Critical Control Point (CCP): A point, step or procedure where you can intervene to prevent, control, or eliminate the growth of micro-organisms before the food is served to customers.

Critical Limit: Minimum and maximum limits that the CCP must meet in order to prevent, eliminate, or reduce a hazard to an acceptable limit.

Cross-Connection: A physical link through which contaminants from drains, sewers, or wastewater can enter a potable water supply. A hose connected to a water supply and submerged into a mop bucket is an example.

Cross-Contamination: The transfer of harmful substances or micro-organisms to food from other foods, people or surfaces.

Cryptosporidiosis: Sometimes referred to as "crypto". A waterborne disease caused by the ingestion of parasites whose symptoms include diarrhea. In immune compromised people, such as HIV/AIDS patients, infection can cause permanent and life threatening diarrhea.

Cyclosporiasis: A waterborne disease caused by parasites that has been linked to fresh produce whose main symptom is watery diarrhea. In the past, Cyclospora infection was usually found in people who lived or traveled in developing countries. In the last several years, outbreaks of cyclosporiasis have been reported in the United States and Canada.

D

Data Logger: A unit that records air temperature at pre-set intervals and allows data to be downloaded into a software program. Some models can also take internal temperatures with a probe.

Deep Chilling Storage: Storage used to hold food at a temperature of –3°C to 0°C (27°F to 32°F) for short time periods.

Digital Thermometer: A thermometer that provides a digital read out – sometimes referred to as a thermistor thermometer.

Dimple: An indentation on the stem of a bi-metallic thermometer that indicates how far the stem should be immersed or inserted.

Direct transmission: Direct transmission of foodborne disease occurs when micro-organisms transfer directly from the source to the food through ways such as touching, coughing, or sneezing directly onto the food.

Discard Time: The time at which food must be thrown out.

Distance-to-Spot Ratio: The size of the area being evaluated by an infrared thermometer as it relates to distance.

Dry Lab: To record data without actually measuring it, for example food temperatures.

Dry Storage: The holding of non-perishable food items, such as rice, flour, crackers and canned goods at 50 to 60 percent humidity and between 10°C and 21°C (50°F and 70°F).

E

Expiration date: Date on a package or label that shows how long the food is good. Food should be dicarded after the expiration date. (Example: Baby food, nutritional supplements)

F

FAT-TOM: An acronym for the conditions favourable for the growth of bacteria: Food, Acidity, Time, Temperature, Oxygen and Moisture.

Finger Cot: A protective barrier used to cover a properly bandaged cut or wound on the finger.

First In First Out (FIFO): A method of stock rotation in which new supplies are shelved behind old supplies, so the old are used first. All the inventory is marked with either the date the item was received, the expiration date or the date it was prepared.

Flow of Food: The path that food follows throughout a foodservice or food retail operation.

Fly Fans: *See air curtains.*

Foodborne Illness: A disease caused by the ingestion of contaminated food.

Foodborne Infection: An illness that is the direct result of consuming food containing harmful living micro-organisms. Symptoms usually do not appear right away.

Foodborne Intoxication: Results from consuming food containing toxins. The toxin may have been produced by harmful bacteria found on the food or be the result of a chemical contamination. Symptoms usaully appear within a few hours.

Food Bar: A display of hot and/or cold foods where customers either serve themselves or are helped by attendants.

Food Contact Surfaces: Any equipment or utensil surface which normally comes in contact with food or which may drain, drip, or splash in food or on surfaces normally in contact with food. Cutting boards, knives, and splash areas are examples of food-contact surfaces.

Food-Grade Container: A container that will not transfer harmful substances to the food it is holding.

Food Retail and Food Services Code (FRFSC): A model food code that provides a common set of harmonized food-safety standards and operational guidelines, which are recognized by the government, the food industry and consumers.

Four Hour Rule: Potentially hazardous foods may not be exposed to the temperature danger zone for more than four hours. The exposure time accumulates during each stage of handling — from the time food arrives at the receiving dock to the time it is cooked. Exposure time begins again when the food is held for service, cooled and reheated.

Fungi: A group of micro-organisms that include moulds, yeasts and mushrooms.

G

Gastrointestinal Illness: An illness relating to the stomach or intestine.

Glue Boards: Cardboard containers open at both ends that are used to catch pests. The glue on the floor of the trap holds roaches or rodents as they enter the trap.

Group Training: Involves a group of trainees meeting with a trainer, usually in a session apart from their normal work.

H

Hair Restraint: A device used to keep food handler's hair away from food and to keep food handlers from touching their hair.

Hand Sanitizer: A liquid used to lower the number of micro-organisms on the surface of the skin. Hand sanitizers should be used after proper hand washing, not in place of it.

Hazard Analysis Critical Control Point (HACCP): A food-safety system designed to keep food safe throughout its flow in an establishment. HACCP is based on the idea that if hazards are identified at specific points in a food's flow, the hazards can be prevented, eliminated or reduced to safe levels.

Hazard Analysis: The process of identifying and evaluating potential hazards associated with foods in order to decide which foods must be addressed in a HACCP plan.

Hazard: Any agent or condition that may contaminate food at any time during its flow through a foodservice operation. Hazards include micro-organisms that can grow during preparation, storage, and/or holding; micro-organisms or toxins that can survive heating; chemicals and objects that can contaminate food or food contact surfaces.

Heat Sanitizing: The most common way to heat sanitize tableware, utensils or equipment is to submerge or spray these items with hot water.

High Risk Populations: People who have a greater risk of developing foodborne illness due to weakened immune systems.

Hot-Holding Equipment: Equipment such as bains maries, chafing dishes, steam tables and heated cabinets designed to hold foods at temperatures of 60°C (140°F) or above. This equipment is not designed to heat foods.

I

Ice Wand: A plastic paddle filled with water and frozen.

Ice-Water Bath: A method of cooling food in which a container holding hot food is placed inside a larger container of ice water. The ice surrounding the hot food container disperses the heat quickly.

Incident: A situation where a case of foodborne illness can be isolated to one person. There are no other related cases

Indirect transmission: Describes a situation in which harmful substances travel from one surface or food to another.

Infected Lesion: A wound or injury that is contaminated with a pathogen.

Infestation: The situation when pests overrun or inhabit an establishment in large numbers.

Infrared Thermometer: A non-contact thermometer that measures surface temperature using infrared or laser technology.

Integrated Pest Management (IPM): A decision-making process that uses control measures to prevent pests from entering your facility and eliminate existing pest infestations in an effective, economic and environmentally sound manner.

Iodine: A chemical sanitizer considered to be one of the most effective. Less corrosive and irritating to skin than chlorine.

L

Law: Rules and regulations established by federal, provincial and local authorities.

Layout: The order of equipment, work areas and furniture for dining and back-of-the-house areas.

Lot Code: The lot code is a serialized number printed on an individual container. This serves as a reference or identifying number to track production information.

Lux: Lux is the International System of Units of illumination. Lux is equal to one lumen per square metre, and equivalent to .0929 foot-candles. approximately 50 foot-candles is equivalent to 549 lux.

M

Master Cleaning Schedule: A comprehensive chart that outlines cleaning duties and procedures.

Material Safety Data Sheet (MSDS): A sheet that lists the chemical and common name of the material, potential physical and health hazards and direction for safe handling and use.

Micro-Organisms: Small life forms that can be seen only with a microscope, that may cause a disease. Examples include bacteria, viruses, parasites and fungi.

Minimum Internal Temperature: The required cooking temperature that the internal portion of food must meet in order to sufficiently reduce the number of micro-organisms that might be present. This temperature is specific to the type of food being cooked. Foods must reach and hold a minimum temperature for a specified amount of time.

Mobile Vending Units: A cart, stand or kiosk that is operated either from a fixed location or on an established daily route, from which food is served or provided to the public with or without charge.

Modified Atmosphere Packaging (MAP) foods: MAP is a packaging process by which air is removed from a food package and replaced with gases such as carbon dioxide and nitrogen. These gases help extend the products' shelf life.

Mould: A type of fungus that causes food spoilage. Some moulds produce toxins that can cause foodborne spoilage.

O

One-Stage Cooling: A process used for cooling food prepared at room temperature from 20°C (68°F) to 4°C (40°F) or less in four hours.

Outbreak: An incident in which two or more people experience the same illness after eating the same food or drinking the same water. Laboratory analysis must show that the food is the source of the illness.

Outbreak Response: Includes actions that investigate, decrease and contain a foodborne outbreak, as well as risk communication activities.

P

Parasite: A micro-organism that needs to live in or on a host to survive.

Pathogen: A disease-causing micro-organism.

Personal Hygiene: Sanitary health habits that include keeping the body and hair clean, wearing clean clothes and washing hands regularly.

Pest Control Operator: A licensed or certified technician who implements and monitors control programs for companies that contract for services.

Pesticide: A product that controls, destroys or inhibits the activity of pests.

pH: A measure of acidity or alkalinity. The pH scale ranges from 0 to 14. A ph below 7 is acidic and above 7 is alkaline.

Physical Hazard: A type of contamination that results from the accidental introduction of foreign objects into foods.

Pooled Eggs: The practice of combining several cracked eggs in a common container.

Potable Water: Water that is safe to drink or to use as an ingredient in food.

Potentially Hazardous Food: Food that requires temperature control and is likely to support the growth of pathogenic micro-organisms or the formation of toxins; foods that can easily support the growth of bacteria. These foods are most often moist, high in protein, and have a neutral pH. They are also foods that have been associated with a foodborne illness.

Probe: The sensing area of a thermometer.

Public Health Inspector: Also known as Environmental Health Officer. An individual trained in sanitation, food safety and public health principles and methods. Public health inspectors are involved in most of the aspects of a foodservice operation from conducting periodic inspections to ensure compliance to educating the managers and food handlers in food safety.

Q

Quaternary Ammonium Compounds (quats): A group of sanitizers all having the same basic chemical structure. Quats are generally non-toxic, non-corrosive and stable when exposed to heat but may not kill certain types of micro-organisms.

R

Ready-to-Eat Foods: Potentially hazardous food that is edible without washing, cooking, or additional preparation by the food establishment or consumer, and/or food that has been pre-cooked to the temperature and time required for that specific food.

Recall: The isolation and removal of an unsafe food from the distribution chain. This food has been released from a manufacturer's direct control, and is under the control of others in storage, distribution or retail, and extends to food sold to consumers.

Recovery Rate: The length of time it takes to produce hot water once a water heater's supply is low enough to start refilling.

Regulation: Rules established to outline specific requirements, often labeled an "act".

Residual Spray: A spray which insects absorb as they come into contact with it.

Re-Work: To recycle processed food.

Risk: The chance that a given condition will lead to a hazard.

Risk Management: The act or practice of controlling risk.

S

Sanitary: Free of harmful levels of contamination.

Sanitizing: The process of reducing the number of micro-organisms on a surface to safe levels.

Sanitizing Lotion: A liquid used to lower the number of micro-organisms on the surface of the skin.

Scombroid Poisoning: An illness that occurs when a person eats a scombroid fish that has been time-temperature abused. Scrombroid fish include tuna, mackerel, bluefish, skipjack and bonito.

Shelf Life: Recommended period of time during which a material may be stored and remain suitable for use.

Single-Use Gloves: Disposable gloves used to provide a barrier between the hands and the food they come in contact with. Gloves should never be used in place of hand washing. Food handlers should wash their hands when putting on gloves and when changing to a fresh pair.

Sneeze Guard: A food shield placed in a direct line between food on display and the mouth/nose of a person of average height, usually fourteen to forty-eight inches above the food.

Sous-Vide Foods: Foods processed by this method are vacuum-packaged in individual pouches, partially or fully cooked and then chilled. These foods are often heated for service in the establishment.

Specifications: A detailed, organized outline of ingredients, recipes, products and packaging materials.

Spores: Thick protective structures formed by certain bacteria in response to adverse conditions. Spores are highly resistant and survive cooking, freezing and some sanitizing mixtures.

T

Temperature Danger Zone: The temperature range between 4°C and 60°C (40°F to 140°F) within which most bacteria grow and reproduce.

Temporary Units: A unit that is licensed to operate in a specific location for a certain period of time, usually not exceeding 14 consecutive days, in connection with a single event or celebration. Licenses may extend for an entire season.

Thermocouple: A digital read, hand held thermometer that provides quick temperature readings through a sensor on the tip of the stem.

Time-Temperature Abuse: Abuse or violation has occurred when potentially hazardous food is exposed to the temperature danger zone of 4°C to 60°C (40°F to 140°F) for any amount of time. Foods being prepared, cooked, cooled and reheated should be passed through the temperature danger zone as quickly as possible to avoid growth of disease causing micro-organisms.

Time-Temperature Indicator (TTI): A time and temperature monitoring device that is a strip of liquid crystals that is attached to food shipments and changes colour when the goods reach unsafe temperatures.

Toxin-Mediated Infection: This occurs when a person eats a food that contains pathogens, which then produce illness causing toxins in the intestines.

Toxins: Are poisons that are produced by micro-organisms, carried by fish, or released by plants.

Two-Stage Cooling: A process used to cool hot foods in two stages: from 60°C (140°F) to 20°C (68°F) in two hours or less; and from 20°C (68°F) to 4°C (40°F) in four hours or less.

U

UHT Foods: These foods are heat treated at very high temperatures (pasteurized) for a short time to kill micro-organisms that can cause illness. These foods are then packaged under sterile conditions. UHT foods can be stored at room temperature if unopened.

Ultra-Pasteurized Packaged Foods: Ultra-pasteurized foods, such as milk products in cartons, have been heat treated to kill disease-causing micro-organisms. Foods labeled UHT have been ultra-pasteurized (high temperature/short time)

and aseptically packaged (hermetically sealed).

V

Vacuum-Packaged Foods: Vacuum packaging is the process of removing air from around a food product sealed in a package. This process increases the shelf life of the product.

Variances: Changes or suspensions of the rules for a specific procedure or part of the restaurant.

Vegetative Cells: Cells that can grow and reproduce.

Vehicle: An item, such as wind, water, human hands, or dirty utensils that carries or transports disease-causing micro-organisms.

Vending Machines: Money-, card-, or key-operated self-service devices that dispense servings of food in bulk or in packages.

Virus: One of the smallest and simplest micro-organisms. Viruses are usually transmitted to food from the foodhandler.

W

Water Activity: The amount of moisture in food available for the growth of micro-organisms. Potentially hazardous foods have water activity values of 0.85 or above. Expressed as a_w.

Workflow: The order of the tasks in preparing a food item, beginning in the receiving area and leading to the dining room.

Workplace Hazardous Materials Information System (WHMIS): An information system designed to protect the health and safety of employees involved in the purchase, storage or use of potentially hazardous chemicals.

Y

Yeasts: Fungi that require sugar and moisture to survive. They spoil foods, such as jellies and honey, by feeding on the sugar these foods contain.

ANSWER KEY

SOLUTIONS AND PAGE REFERENCES

CHAPTER ONE

True/False (page 10)	Exercise (page 18)
1. False	1. a
2. True	2. c
3. False	3. b
4. True	4. d
5. True	5. c
	6. d
	7. c
	8. b

CHAPTER TWO

True/False (page 19)	Exercise (page 40)
1. True	1. d
2. False	2. d
3. True	3. b
4. False	4. c
5. True	5. d
	6. d
	7. d
	8. d

CHAPTER FIVE

True/False (page 62)	Exercise (page 72)
1. True	1. a
2. False	2. c
3. False	3. c
4. False	4. b
5. False	5. b
	6. d
	7. c
	8. c

CHAPTER SIX

True/False (page 73)	Exercise (page 82)
1. False	1. a
2. False	2. b
3. False	3. c
4. True	4. b
5. False	5. a
	6. b
	7. d
	8. c

CHAPTER THREE

True/False) (page 41)	Exercise (page 50)
1. True	1. a
2. False	2. c
3. False	3. b
4. True	4. a
5. False	5. d
	6. b
	7. c
	8. d

CHAPTER FOUR

True/False (page 52)	Exercise (page 61)
1. False	1. a
2. False	2. a
3. False	3. d
4. False	4. c
5. True	5. c
	6. d
	7. a
	8. a

CHAPTER SEVEN

True/False) (page 83)	Exercise (page 100)
1. False	1. d
2. True	2. c
3. False	3. a
4. False	4. c
5. False	5. c
	6. d
	7. a
	8. b

CHAPTER EIGHT

True/False (page 102)	Exercise (page 114)
1. False	1. c
2. False	2. a
3. False	3. d
4. True	4. a
5. True	5. c
	6. b
	7. c
	8. b

CHAPTER NINE

True/False (page 115)

1. False
2. False
3. True
4. False
5. False

Exercise (page 122)

1. c
2. d
3. c
4. b
5. d
6. c
7. c
8. a

CHAPTER TEN

True/False (page 123)

1. True
2. False
3. False
4. True
5. False

Exercise (page 133)

1. a
2. b
3. d
4. b
5. d
6. a
7. c
8. c

CHAPTER THIRTEEN

True/False (page 164)

1. False
2. True
3. True
4. False
5. True

Exercise (page 175)

1. a
2. c
3. b
4. a
5. a
6. c
7. b
8. c

CHAPTER FOURTEEN

True/False (page 176)

1. True
2. True
3. True
4. False
5. True

Exercise (page 184)

1. b
2. c
3. d
4. d
5. d
6. a
7. b
8. a

CHAPTER ELEVEN

True/False) (page 136)

1. True
2. False
3. False
4. False
5. True

Exercise (page 148)

1. b
2. b
3. a
4. c
5. b
6. a
7. b
8. c

CHAPTER TWELVE

True/False (page 149)

1. False
2. True
3. True
4. True
5. False

Exercise (page 163)

1. b
2. d
3. b
4. c
5. d
6. a
7. d
8. c

ANSWERS TO CONSIDER THIS...

CHAPTER 1

People contributed to this outbreak, and people could have prevented it. In most restaurants the manager has the greatest responsibility for food safety. Managers can make sure that food handlers know the risks associated with the food they prepare and how to control them.

One factor that led to the outbreak was time-temperature abuse. By only measuring the temperature of the smallest turkey, the chef missed that the others had not reached the proper internal temperature. Since the turkey was not cooked properly, bacteria were not killed. Further, sitting unrefrigerated before delivery let the bacteria grow. The food handler showing up to work ill was another factor that might have contributed to the outbreak. All of these factors are within a manager's control.

Although you might not have been able to guess everything that went wrong in this situation, in the following chapters you will be given information to identify individual problems and prevent them from happening.

CHAPTER 2

The fact that fruits and vegetables are often eaten without cooking makes them potential sources of pathogenic bacteria. Fresh fruits and vegetables are now recognized as one of the most significant sources of foodborne illness. Cantaloupes have been implicated as the source of *Salmonella* in a number of outbreaks in North America in recent years. The melons are grown on the ground where they can be contaminated by rodents, birds and untreated manure or surface water; they can also become contaminated at other points in the farm-to-fork food chain, from contaminated wash water, shipping containers, hands of infected people, etc.

The flesh of cantaloupes can be contaminated when cutting through a contaminated rind. If the cut pieces are held for several hours or days above refrigeration temperatures, there may be growth of *Salmonella*. Although not a high-protein food, cantaloupe has sufficient nutrients and moisture and a low enough acidity to allow the growth of harmful bacteria. When several cantaloupes are cut at one time, one contaminated rind can contaminate the flesh of several cantaloupes. Although the cantaloupe slices were placed on ice in this case, ice, unlike refrigeration, cannot be relied on to maintain the temperature of the cantaloupe flesh that sits above it. Cross-contamination of beef with *Salmonella* likely occurred when the cutting board and knife used to slice the cantaloupes were then used for the beef; not immediately refrigerating the sliced beef may have allowed some growth of the bacteria. Always clean fresh fruits and vegetables even if the skin or rind will not be eaten. Cantaloupes should be scrubbed with a produce brush. Clean cutting boards and utensils after each use and practice good hand hygiene.

Salmonella grows between 6.5°C (44°F) and 47°C (117°F), at pH 4.5 and above. *Salmonella* is found in water and soil and in the intestinal tracts of birds, poultry, pigs and other animals; insects and human carriers can also be sources of *Salmonella*. People and animals may be carriers without showing any symptoms. As few as 15 to 20 bacteria can cause illness in susceptible individuals.

CHAPTER 3

Shigella bacteria are found in the intestinal tract of humans and can contaminate food when infected people do not adequately wash their hands after using the restroom. Some people who are infected may not show symptoms but can still pass the *Shigella* bacteria on to others. *Shigella* bacteria are present in the stools of infected people while they are sick and for up to four weeks after the illness. *Shigella* bacteria are highly infectious – as few as 10 bacteria can cause illness in susceptible individuals.

Foodservice managers/operators must develop and enforce a policy stating that employees who are ill will be assigned to duties that do not involve handling food or will be sent home until they are well and no longer contagious. Employees who have recently been ill should be encouraged to seek medical advice on whether they can safely return to food handling duties despite no longer having symptoms. Joe's should have developed and encouraged open communication with all of its employees so that Sharon would have known to stop handling food when she began to feel ill, and that she should have sought medical advice before beginning work.

Employees must have access to well-equipped hand washing facilities at all times. Soap and single-use paper towels must always be provided. Joe's needs to ensure that all of its employees understand the importance of hand washing and that they must take the time to wash hands properly regardless of other challenges when working a busy shift.

CHAPTER 5

Procedures for purchasing and receiving must be in place so that the safety of food is not jeopardized by bad luck, bad timing, employee vacations or lack of experience. To prevent deliveries from arriving all at the same time, Catherine or her manager needs to set up a time with each supplier to bring the food deliveries when business is slower. Catherine should have asked for a delay in deliveries so that she would have the time to inspect each delivery and get them all into the freezer or refrigerator without delay. All the rules for accepting or rejecting foods could then have been followed. The good reputation of the supplier should never be a reason to not follow these rules.

Deli foods, such as luncheon meats and salads, are seldom cooked or heated prior to serving and so have a greater risk of becoming a health hazard than those that are. Since the refrigeration unit in the delivery truck may not have been functioning properly, the deli foods may have already suffered some temperature abuse. If Catherine had taken the time to measure the products' temperatures, she would have known if the delivery person was just complaining or if he had tipped her off about something of concern. The added time to get the deli foods into refrigeration after delivery because Catherine was busy would have further increased the risk of a food safety problem.

The Consider This...exercise in the next chapter will show how poor receiving practices can impact the safety of the meals served at White Oaks Nursing Home.

CHAPTER 6

A refrigerator is designed to receive cold foods and maintain their temperature. Pete should have cooled the vegetable soup before putting it in the refrigerator. When hot items are placed in a refrigeration unit, the temperature inside the unit can rise into the danger zone (above 4°C [40°F]) which encourages the growth of bacteria. To avoid this rise in temperature, divide large quantities of food into shallow pans and use quick-chilling techniques (*See Chapter 6*) to rapidly cool the food.

The type and capacity of a refrigerator are important. Most refrigerators are cold holding units designed to receive food at 4°C (40°F) or lower and keep them cold. Refrigerators do not have the capacity to receive large amounts of hot food and cool them. Special refrigerators may be necessary for operations that cool large amounts of hot food on a regular basis.

The temperature of a storage area should be checked when there is any concern. When Pete noticed that the refrigerator did not feel quite as cool as normal, he should have checked the temperature inside the refrigerator. If the temperature is elevated, it could be the result of Catherine opening the door several times and placing the warmer delivery items into the refrigerator, or it could be that the refrigerator is not functioning properly.

Catherine did not follow recommended food storage placement in her hurry to get the deliveries into the refrigerator. Fresh produce should not be stored below raw chicken, where juices from the raw chicken could drip on to the produce. The raw chicken should have been stored on the bottom shelf and the fresh produce stored above it. As well, by placing the deli products next to the door which is the warmest area in a refrigerator, Catherine increased the risk of a food safety problem even further since they may have already suffered some temperature abuse (*See Chapter 4*). Outbreaks of listeriosis are linked most often to ready-to-eat foods such as deli meats, pâté and soft cheeses. *Listeria monocytogenes* can grow at low temperatures. Anyone can get listeriosis, but those at highest risk are newborns, the elderly, people with weakened immune systems and pregnant women.

CHAPTER 7

Bacillus cereus is a spore-forming bacterium that can cause diarrhoeal or emetic (vomiting) foodborne illness if it is present in high numbers in food. Illness results when foods containing the emetic or diarrhoeal toxin are eaten or when the diarrhoeal toxin is released in the intestine after consuming foods containing the bacteria or its spores. The emetic toxin is heat-stable while the diarrhoeal toxin is destroyed by heat. *B. cereus* grows in the temperature range of 10°C to 49°C (50°F to 120°F). In the emetic type of *B. cereus* gastroenteritis, the onset of illness can be as short as 30 minutes and symptoms can persist for as long as 24 hours.

B. cereus is frequently present in uncooked rice, and heat-resistant spores may survive cooking. If cooked rice is held at room temperature, bacterial growth can occur and a heat-stable toxin is produced that can survive brief heating, such as stir-frying. In the outbreak described in this Consider This..., the bacterial growth would have probably occurred at the restaurant and when the fried rice was transported to the school.

Cooked rice is a potentially hazardous food. Once cooked, the rice should have been cooled rapidly and immediately placed in the refrigerator. When transporting the fried rice and the other foods to the school, precautions were not taken to ensure that food temperatures were kept out of the danger zone (4°C - 60°C or 40°F - 140°F).

CHAPTER 8

The meringue that James had made for the pies was a potentially hazardous food as it was made with uncooked eggs. Potentially hazardous foods must be kept out of temperatures that support the growth of bacteria. Since the pies were usually made in the morning, and the popular dish was immediately eaten after hitting the buffet the refrigeration step was not included in the recipe.

To make sure this error is not repeated, Esquire's management staff needs to develop a plan looking at all the risks associated with their dishes. It is important that they let their staff know how long the meringue pies can safely be left unrefrigerated. Procedures that explicitly require the refrigeration of the dessert and specify what to do if preparing them prior to service must be written into the recipe. Esquire's staff should be involved in the development of these guidelines so they can be exposed to why it is important.

CHAPTER 10

Sloppy food handling and a lack of quick refrigeration at a safe temperature provided the ideal conditions for *Staphylococcus aureus* intoxication. The quantity of lunch boxes produced for this event was more than Terry's pub routinely produced, resulting in difficulty following recommended food-handling guidelines.

The bento boxes were not refrigerated or kept cool from preparation through to delivery along the route.

The food was held at room temperature long enough to allow the bacteria to multiply and produce toxins. Normal cooking temperatures cannot destroy the toxins produced by *Staphylococcus aureus*.

This case emphasizes the risk of storing food at room temperature for long periods and allowing untrained, potentially infected food handlers to prepare food.

CHAPTER 11

Detergents, cleaning compounds, drain cleaners, polishes and sanitizers are common chemicals necessary for the maintenance of sanitary conditions in a food service establishment. Care must be taken to ensure these chemicals do not contaminate food and beverages, causing illness.

In this case, the pipe connection to the ice-making machine lacked an air gap to prevent backflow. This allowed wastewater, detergent and drain cleaner to back up into the ice cube bin, contaminating the ice used for drinks.

Ice bins and drain lines used for dispensing drink machines must be protected by approved air gaps. The manager needs to consult a licensed plumber to correct the plumbing system problem.

CHAPTER 12

Researchers have recently suggested that certain foods—especially cheese and milk—can be safe havens for bacteria when they are dried onto tableware. Bacteria like *E. coli* can survive for long periods of time if they make their way into food dried onto dishes. If those dishes aren't thoroughly washed, they can sometimes cause foodborne disease outbreaks. Cheesy forks can be the most problematic utensils, and milk dried onto glasses protects bacteria more than any other food.

The tableware can be washed, rinsed and sanitized in a three-compartment sink using hot water and a chemical sanitizer. All three sinks must be cleaned and sanitized to destroy potential contaminants; this is especially important if the sinks have not been used for a while. The tableware can be pre-soaked and washed in the first compartment and rinsed in the second. Water in both sinks must be at least 45°C (113°F). Chemical sanitizing can be done in the third sink, using the correct concentration and should be done for at least two minutes, at a temperature appropriate to the chemical used.

Tableware and equipment should always be air-dried. Towel drying tableware can remove the chemical sanitizer before it has fully worked to kill any micro-organisms. Unsanitary towels can also transfer micro-organisms from dirty to clean tableware.

CHAPTER 13

Older buildings often have areas where pests (including rodents and insects) can hide that should have been corrected through remodeling. Decaying outer building materials and problematic neighbours can make pest control hard. Jeb needs to bring his Food Network contractors in to seal pipe openings and crevices around the sinks with a proper sealant. All cracks and crevices in the walls, floors, doors and window frames in the storage areas should also be sealed. A further check for new cracks and openings should also be added to the self-inspections.

Garbage should be removed many times throughout the day so the rats do not have a constant area to eat and hide. Garbage containers should be cleaned and sanitized after each load is emptied. Recyclables should be rinsed and stored in a sanitary manner until pick-up to avoid insect infestation.

Jeb should call a licensed and registered pest-control operator to help him with traps and identifying problem areas. The pest control operator will be able to work with Jeb to develop an integrated pest management (IPM) program to address sanitation and structural flaws. The IPM program will also provide Jeb with a set of non-chemical and safe chemical control methods to ensure that the problem is taken care of. As part of the program Jeb should also contact the businesses that share the building and encourage them to work on the rat problem together.

CHAPTER 14

An inspection serves as a test of how well a food safety system is working. In this case, Gerry has thought about and implemented a good system. Gerry knows about the risks that are associated with his dishes, he stays on top of changing ingredients and this is reflected in his documentation.

Gerry knew that the chicken souvlaki was a dish that contained potentially hazardous food. He had designed a flowchart, setting up CCPs and corrective actions. He

co-operated with Peter throughout the inspection and encouraged a dialogue with him about how to improve his systems. Gerry took advantage of having a food safety expert in his restaurant by asking him how to avoid what happened to his competitor.

Gerry should continue to conduct his own self-inspections and monitor his procedures to test how well his system is working. It's important that the correct practices are being carried out all the time, not just when the inspector is present. If corrective actions occur frequently, he may need to retrain some of his employees to follow the procedures. Gerry may also want to bring Peter in to talk with his staff about why following safe food handling and preparation steps are important.

INDEX

This index references both chapter and page number. For example, information on abrasive cleaners can be found in chapter 12, on page 152.

inspection procedures, 14-180
    pest, 13-171
    purchasing and receiving, 5-62, 5-63
    regulatory agencies and inspections,
    14-176, 14-179 to 14-181
inspection stamps, 5-65
inspector: *see Public Health Inspector*
institutional-service operation, 10-124
integrated pest management,
    access, 13-165 to 13-167
    basic rules, 13-164
    definition, 13-165
    food and shelter, denial of, 13-166, 13-167
    identifying pests, 13-168 to 13-170
    using pesticides, 13-173
iodine sanitizer, 12-150, 12-153, 12-155
    iodophors, 12-150, 12-153
IPM: *see integrated pest management*

J
jaundice, 3-48
jewelry, 3-46

K
kitchen,
    cleaning and sanitizing equipment, 12-157
    equipment standards, 11-140
    flooring, 11-139, 11-140

L
labeling
    allergens, 2-35
    chemical, 2-31
    holding food, 7-91, 7-95
    self-service , 7-96, 10-125
    storage, 6-73, 6-74
lamb: see meats
laser thermometer: *see infrared thermometer*
layout, 11-136, 11-137
law, 14-177
leftovers, 7-87
lighting, 11-143
listeriosis, 2-28

liquids,
    measuring temperature, 4-57
    cooling, 7-93
lobster,
    see shellfish
lot code, 5-63, 5-64, 5-66
lux, 11-143

M
major foodborne illness, 2-22, 2-28, 2-29
manager, 1-10
MAP: *see modified atmosphere packaging*
master cleaning schedule, 12-150, 12-161
material safety data sheet, 9-117, B-189
    hazardous materials, 12-160
meat,
    beef, 5-65, 7-89
    cooking, 7-89
    grades, 5-65
    ground meat, 6-75, 7-89, 8-105, 8-106
    lamb, 5-65, 7-89
    pork, 5-65, 7-80
    potentially hazardous food, 1-11, 1-12
    preparation, 7-83, 7-86, 7-87
    receiving, 5-65
    stamp, 5-65
    storage, 6-73, 6-75, 6-77
    veal, 7-89
    water activity level, 2-23
melon, 1-12, 1-13, 7-87
menu,
    HACCP system, 8-104
micro-organism,
    bacteria, 1-13, 2-19
    cooking food, 7-89
    cooling food, 7-91, 7-92
    cross contamination, 1-11, 1-14
    cleaning and sanitizing, 12-149
    FAT-TOM, 2-23
    foodborne infection and intoxication, 2-22
    foodhandling, 7-83, 7-87
    fungi, 2-26
    growth conditions, 2-20 to 2-23

handwashing, 3-44, 3-45
mould, 2-26
parasites, 2-25
pest control, 13-164, 13-168
refrigerated storage, 6-75
thawing food, 7-84
time and temperature control, 2-23, 7-83
viruses, 1-13, 2-25
yeasts, 2-26
microwave
cooking, 7-90
thawing, 7-85
milk: *see dairy products*
minimum internal temperatures, 7-84, 7-89
mobile vending units, 10-124, 10-129
modified atmosphere packaging, 5-63
receiving, 5-68
storing, 6-79
moisture,
bacteria reproduction, 2-23
mould, 2-26
mollusck: *see shellfish*
monitoring procedures, 8-109
MSDS: *see material safety data sheet*
mushroom, 2-26
mussels: *see shellfish*

N

nail polish, 3-45
National Sanitation Foundation: see NSF international
norovirus, 2-24, 2-25
norwalk virus: *see norovirus*
NSF International, 11-140

O

off-site delivery, 10-126
proper containers for transporting food,
10-127, 10-128
one-stage cooling, 7-84, 7-92
on-site delivery, 10-125
outbreak, 1-16, 9-116, 9-118
outbreak response, 9-116, 9-119, 9-120
outdoor service, 10-128

oxygen, bacterial growth, 2-23
oysters: *see shellfish*

P

packaged food, 5-63, 5-68
temperature, 4-57
parasite, 1-13, 2-20, 2-25, 2-26
pathogen, 2-19, 2-20
pasteurized,
dairy products, 5-67, 10-125
shell eggs, 5-66, 10-125
UHT foods, 5-63
personal hygiene,
contamination, 1-16
definition, 3-42
dressing area and restrooms, 3-47
eating and drinking, 3-45
hand care, 3-45
handwashing, 3-43, 3-44
illness and injury, 3-47
pest control: *see integrated pest management*
pest control operator, 13-165, 13-170
pesticide, 13-165
chemical hazard, 1-13, 2-30
integrated pest management, 13-173
pests,
signs of, 13-168
pH,
chemical sanitizers, 12-155
FAT-TOM, 2-23
water, 12-151
physical hazards, 1-14, 2-20, 2-31
pipe, 13-167
plant toxin, 2-27
plumbing, 11-144
pooled eggs, 7-84, 7-86
pork: *see meat*
portable equipment, 11-142
potable water, 7-84
cross-connections, 11-137, 11-144
fruit and vegetables, 7-87
plumbing, 11-144
thawing, 7-85